Richard G. Hodgson
A·D. 1963 July 22

THE PLANET MERCURY

Observing the transit of Mercury, using projection method.
Madrid Observatory, 1953

The Planet Mercury

*

Dr. WERNER SANDNER

Translated by
ALEX HELM, F.R.A.S.

FABER AND FABER
24 Russell Square
London

First published in mcmlxiii
by Faber and Faber Limited
24 Russell Square, London, W.C.1
Printed in Great Britain
by Ebenezer Baylis and Son, Limited
The Trinity Press, Worcester, and London

Contents

_____ * _____

7

Illustrations

---- * ----

9

Illustrations

I

In the Beginning

---------- * ----------

Of all the major planets, Mercury is the most difficult to
observe with the naked eye. This is particularly so in the
middle and higher latitudes, where the planet is never far
above the mist of the horizon after sunset, and it is
eminently possible that many an active astronomer has
to date been unable to catch a glimpse of elusive Mercury, although the statement said to have been made by
Copernicus (1473–1543) on his death-bed, that he had
never succeeded in seeing that planet, probably belongs
to the realms of fable. On the same point, Kepler's tutor,
Mästlin (1550–1631), once summed up the difficulties
entailed, when he said that Mercury seemed to have
been created for the sole purpose of discrediting astronomers.

There can be no doubt that Mercury was a familiar
object to astronomers of the early cultures of the Orient
where viewing conditions, particularly for this planet, are
far more favourable. Mercury was also known to the
Germanic peoples, and moreover the knowledge was not
confined only to the Nordic seafarers, among whom such
a knowledge would hardly be surprising, since they often
penetrated well into the southern latitudes, as far as the
shores of North Africa. There is evidence to show that
learned men living in western central Europe during the
time of the Roman Empire were aware of the existence

of this planet. Here Mercury was connected with the deity Wodan, or Odin among the Scandinavian races.

Among the Indo-Germanic peoples of ancient Italy the planet Mercury was given the name 'Boudha' (a name which incidentally has nothing whatsoever to do with 'Buddha', the founder of the religion). The word 'Boudha' in fact comes from the same root as the German name Wodan, or Odin. Sometimes the planet was also called 'Rohinêja'.

To the ancient Egyptians Mercury was known as 'Sobkou'; to the Sumerians as 'Bi-ib-bou', while among the ancient Assyrians, Chaldeans and Babylonians it was known as 'Goud-oud', 'Ninib' and 'Nabou', or 'Nebo'; the Phoenicians called it 'Mokim', or 'Monim'. The god Nebo was the scribe who kept the book of fate, and on Chaldean monuments Mercury is depicted as a godhead in regal robes and wearing a tiara; he is often also shown with wings, symbolizing his speed of movement. In Greece during the Classical period, the planet was known as Ερμῆς (Hermes), who was the Greek equivalent of the Roman Mercury.

It was the ancient Egyptians who first realized that the planet Mercury, like Venus, travelled round the Sun, and later the Pythagoreans also adopted this idea. Although ancient cuneiform writings from the valleys of the Tigris and Euphrates indicate observations of Mercury, the oldest definitely dated observation is put at 15th November 265 B.C. From the first thousand years after the birth of Christ we have record of thirty-seven observations by Chinese astronomers, among which there is one dating from 9th June A.D. 118, when Mercury was situated only one degree from the star-cluster known as Praesepe in the constellation of Cancer. The Chinese were always careful to record with the utmost accuracy anything out of the ordinary which they happened to observe in the sky.

During the Middle Ages, the Arabs took the lead in astronomical studies. They called Mercury 'Kokab Outharid', and the Turks also called it 'Outharid', although other names were also current.

The astrologers gave Mercury various attributes during the course of time. Ancient cuneiform writings

Merkur

Fig. 1. Mercury as depicted in the *Deutsch Kalendar* published in Ulm, Germany, in 1498.

describe him as a bringer of luck; a Babylonian inscription addresses him in the following words: 'Star Mercury, who lettest the rains pour down . . .' But so far as later astrologers were concerned, Mercury was sometimes considered lucky, and sometimes unlucky, according to how it was placed relative to the other planets in the sky. In medieval Europe Mercury was usually thought of as a 'sidus dolosum'; in contrast, the Arabs thought that he could bestow riches on his children. All in all, opinions of his influence on men's affairs differed widely.

The symbol which came into use during the Middle Ages to denote Mercury was that of quicksilver, whose easy flow was thought to be apt for this fleet-footed planet. At first the sign was written ☿, although in later times with the addition of the cross it became ☿.

The other thing that remains to be mentioned is that the fourth day of the week has been dedicated to Mercury. In French 'mercredi' comes from the Latin 'Mercurii dies'; Wednesday in English is derived from Wodan's day, while in old Norse it is 'Odinsdagr' from which Swedes and Danes get 'onsdag'.

II

A Strange Celestial Object

———————————— * ————————————

The reason why observation of Mercury in the temperate latitudes is not easy is due to the nature of the planet's orbit. Of all the major planets Mercury lies closest to the Sun, and travels round the Sun inside the orbit of the Earth once in eighty-eight of our days. If one were to travel outward from the Sun, one would first of all cross the path of Mercury, then that of Venus, while the third path is that of the Earth; beyond this the other planets pursue their various orbits. The diagram on page 16 shows the orbits of the first three, drawn to scale.

Seen from the Sun, Mercury is thus the first planet, while Earth is the third. In consequence, so far as any terrestrial observer is concerned, Mercury can never lie in the opposite direction to the Sun, i.e. in opposition; nor is Mercury ever very far from the Sun. This means that Mercury always appears either to rise shortly before the Sun, or to set shortly after it, and is never visible during the middle of the night. Thus we can only see Mercury shining in the twilight of the westerly horizon in the evening, or the easterly horizon in the morning. Just how far it seems to wander from the Sun as seen from Earth (measured in degrees of arc) can easily be seen from the diagram, if one draws the tangent from a given point on the Earth's orbit to the orbit of Mercury. It will be noticed that, at best, Mercury is never more than

28 degrees from the Sun in the plane of the ecliptic, and so, as a result, it is always shrouded in the haze of the horizon during the period of darkness. The point of time when the planet appears furthest from the Sun is known as its 'maximum elongation'.

The further one moves north or south from the equator

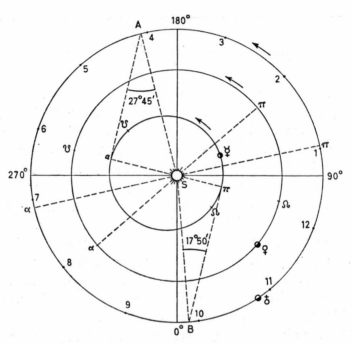

Fig. 2. Orbits of Mercury, Venus and the Earth

on the Earth's surface, the more unfavourable the observing conditions become. In the tropics, where the ecliptic is never more than $23\frac{1}{2}$ degrees out of the vertical relative to the horizon at any time of the year, and the twilight periods are of extremely short duration, Mercury is a fairly easy telescopic object; but in the temperate zones, and to greater degree in the higher latitudes, the inclination of the ecliptic is so acute, that even at the time of maximum elongation Mercury does not appear more than a relatively short distance above the horizon during the period of darkness.

Observational conditions are rendered still more unfavourable by the fact that Mercury's orbit deviates considerably from the circular. Astronomers say that the orbit has a marked 'eccentricity'. In the diagram on p. 16 the two extreme positions for morning visibility, or westerly elongation (Mercury lying west of the Sun) are shown. One can see that at the beginning of April under most favourable conditions, Mercury can be as much as 27 degrees 45 minutes of arc from the Sun; on the other hand, at the beginning of September, under least favourable conditions, the value can be as low as 17 degrees 50 minutes. For evening visibility (easterly elongation, since Mercury then lies east of the Sun) the circumstances are reversed; the maximum possible apparent distance from the Sun occurs in the autumn, while the smallest distance at the time of greatest elongation comes in the spring.

In addition, the best time of the year for evening visibility for an observer in the northern hemisphere is during spring, while autumn is the best time of year for morning observation. In the spring the Sun appears to move northwards. The result of this is that, during evening visibility, Mercury precedes the Sun in the ecliptic; that is to say, it lies further north than the Sun, and so stands higher above the horizon so far as European observers are concerned. In the autumn the situation is reversed; the Sun is moving southward along the ecliptic; during evening visibility Mercury lies more southerly than the Sun, and thus will not rise so high above the horizon. On the other hand, for morning observation it lies further north and thus offers more favourable opportunity in the autumn.

The mean distance of Mercury from the Sun is 36 million miles, which is equivalent to 0·387 astronomical units, one astronomical unit being the mean distance of the Earth from the Sun. However, as a result of the eccentricity of the Mercurian orbit, the planet lies 43 million miles from the Sun during aphelion, i.e. the point of its orbit furthest from the Sun, while the distance

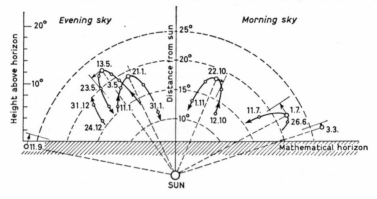

Fig. 3. Elongations of Mercury during 1962.

is only 29 million miles at perihelion, i.e. the point in the orbit nearest the Sun. The difference between these two values is thus fairly considerable. The inclination of the orbit of Mercury relative to the plane of the ecliptic is 7 degrees, and as such the greatest of all the major planets (apart from Pluto, which may, or may not be a true major planet).

Mercury completes one orbit of the Sun in approximately 88 days (the exact figure is actually 87·969 of our days). This means that the Mercurian year is equivalent to $12\frac{1}{2}$ Earth weeks. Mercury travels along its orbit round the Sun at a mean velocity of 29·8 miles per second, whereas the equivalent for Earth is 18·6 miles per second. Kepler's second law shows that the velocity of a planet is greater at perihelion than at aphelion. While the differences in velocity at these two times is not very marked in the cases of Earth and Venus, it is considerable in the case of Mercury, on account of the greater eccentricity of the latter's orbit. At perihelion the velocity of the little planet is 35·4 miles, while at aphelion only 24·2 miles per second.

The short duration of the Mercurian 'year' means that, seen from Earth, Mercury appears first on one side of the Sun and then on the other in fairly rapid succession, i.e. as an evening and then as a morning star. Thus the individual observation periods can never be of very long duration, even in the tropics where the geographic and the climatic conditions for observation of this planet are more favourable than in Europe.

Julius Schmidt (1825–1884), who was the director of the Athens Observatory from 1858 onwards and whose 'Chart of the Mountains of the Moon' brought him fame, said that in the clear skies of Greece he was able to observe Mercury with the naked eye on numerous occasions, but never for periods longer than twenty consecutive days. Also during the last century, Beauchamp, observing in Baghdad, reported that during elongations of the planet he could regularly find Mercury in the evenings or mornings without undue difficulty.

In our latitudes, however, weather permitting, there are perhaps some thirty odd days during the year when Mercury can be seen either as a morning, or an evening star with the naked eye for about half an hour at a time; thus the total time for viewing the planet is in theory only about fifteen hours a year—which makes Mercury a rare object indeed.

A Strange Celestial Object

Generally speaking, it is true to say that Mercury will almost never be noticed by an observer who is not making a special search for it. The best method is to consult some annual publication, such as the *Handbook of the British Astronomical Association*,* and to look up the most favourable dates. For some days to either side of maximum elongation it should be possible to make out the planet—provided that the sky near the horizon is clear of cloud or mist and that there are no artificial lights anywhere in the vicinity. The city-dweller who looks for Mercury from beneath the glow produced by street-lighting and neon advertising signs is doomed to disappointment.

Now and then matters are made easier by the presence of another more prominent object—perhaps Venus or the Moon. The brighter object may then be used as a guide for locating the more elusive Mercury.

Binoculars are very helpful, and it is often possible to pick out Mercury simply by using low-powered instruments (even field-glasses will do), sweeping along parallel to the horizon until the planet comes into view. And although telescopes of considerable power are required to show even the changing phase, it is always worth while searching for this curious, quick-moving little world as it makes its fleeting appearances in the evening twilight or the morning dawn.

---

*Or *The Yearbook of Astronomy*. Editor: J. G. Porter. Associate Editor: Patrick Moore. Published by Eyre & Spottiswoode.

III

Practical Observations of Mercury

———————————— * ————————————

It is perhaps because viewing conditions are so unfavourable, and also the fact that the planet is not an
easy telescopic object, that Mercury offers a challenge
to the serious observer. There is always the urge to find
out more about this elusive little planet.

Since Mercury is one of the inferior planets, i.e. its
orbit lies within that of the Earth, it shows phases just
like Venus and the Moon; during the time of maximum ⟨ approx,
elongation, for instance, it appears to us as half. The
phases of Mercury were first seen by an Italian named
Zupus on 23rd May 1639, and then independently by
Johannes Hewelke—better known as Hevelius—(1611–
1687) on 22nd November 1644 in Danzig. The discovery
of the phases of Venus in 1610 by Galileo Galilei (1564–
1642) with the recently-invented telescope, and the
subsequent discovery of phases on Mercury, were of
profound significance at the time, because one of the
principal arguments against the Copernican Theory was
that no such phenomenon had been observed for either
planet. The apparent diameter of the disc of Mercury
as seen through a telescope will naturally vary considerably with the distance of the planet from the Earth.
Nevertheless its size is such that the phases are detectable
only by means of telescopes with considerable magnification; Galileo's first telescope was not powerful enough.

21

By means of the apparent diameter and the distance of Mercury from the Earth, we are able to calculate the actual diameter of the planet. In this way it has been calculated that the equatorial diameter of Mercury is 3,100 miles, that is to say approximately three-eighths the diameter of the Earth and only greater by one-third than the Moon. The volume of Mercury is only 0·053 that of the Earth, and its mass 0·055 that of Earth, i.e. about one-twentieth. Knowing the volume and the mass, we can work out the mean density: in the case of Mer-

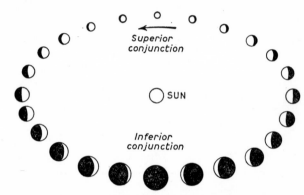

Fig. 4. Mercury as seen from Earth; apparent shape and size at various stages during its orbit round the Sun.

cury this value is 5·72 if one assumes the density of water as one unit, or 1·04 assuming the mean density of the Earth to be one. So far as Mercury is concerned, no flattening at the poles, i.e. no deviation from a true sphere, has as yet been detected; but because of its small size, and turbulences within our own atmosphere, measurements of this kind are extremely difficult to carry out.

It is unfortunate that Mercury is visible to the naked eye only during the twilight period, when it does not stand out well against the still light background of the

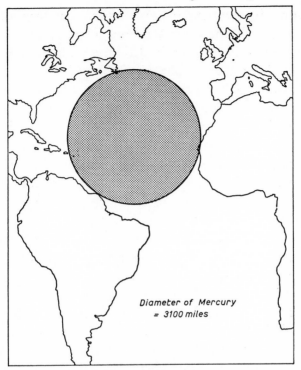

Diameter of Mercury
= 3100 miles

Fig. 5. Size of Mercury compared with north Atlantic
Ocean.

sky. At its brightest Mercury shines more brilliantly than
Sirius, which is the brightest of all the fixed stars, and is
in fact surpassed only by Venus and Jupiter and
occasionally Mars (during a particularly suitable perihelion opposition) among the planets. However, even at
its faintest, it is still as bright as the star Deneb in the
constellation of the Swan, or Aldebaran in the Bull.
Expressed in magnitudes, the brightness of Mercury
varies between $-1 \cdot 6^m$ maximum and $+1 \cdot 7^m$ minimum,
depending on how it is placed relative to the Earth.

From the planet's apparent brightness at any given
time, one can calculate its reflective power, or albedo, if

23

one knows its distance at that particular moment of time from the Earth and from the Sun. The albedo of a body is that proportion of the light falling on a body which it reflects. If the albedo of a given body is equal to 1, we then know that it reflects all the light which it receives; on the other hand, if the value is nil, then the body absorbs all the light and fails to reflect any of it—it would in fact constitute what is known as an 'ideal black body'. In practice, the albedo of a planet thus lies between zero and one. In the case of Mercury, the value is 0·07, which means that the planet reflects only 7 per cent of the light it receives; this is the lowest value for any planet in our Solar System (again with the possible exception of Pluto). From this information we are able to draw certain important conclusions regarding the nature of the surface of the planet, as we shall see later.

Mercury has a distinctly yellowish colour, a fact which was probably first recorded by the astronomer Gruithuisen (1774–1852) in Munich on 6th October 1838. The colour can be seen most clearly when one of the other major planets, Venus for instance, is situated close to Mercury in the sky. A comparison of this sort was, for example, made by the Mexican astronomer, Professor Fr. J. Escalante, in January 1956, when Venus and Mercury appeared in conjunction, close together in the sky. He described the colour of Mercury as 'distinctly yellow' in contrast to the whiteness of Venus. In October 1956 I myself estimated the colour of Mercury equivalent to a value of 6^c (intense yellow) beside Venus, equivalent to 1 (pure white). On the other hand, the well-known German planetary observer, Professor Philipp Fauth (1867–1941) in the *Astronomical Handbook* refers to 'leaden-tinted Mercury' and 'golden-yellow Venus'.

It must also be mentioned that the Russian woman

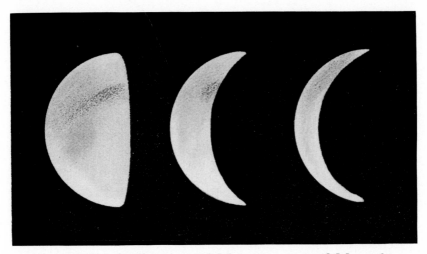

1. 1953 Feb. 28th.   2. 1956 May 1st.   3. 1956 May 7th
I Mercury drawings by Patrick Moore, 6.5-inch reflector

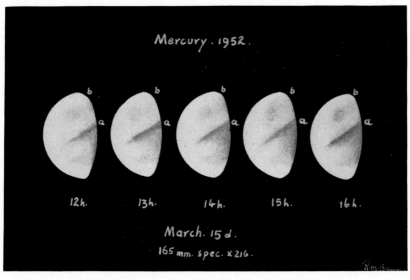

II Mercury drawing by R. M. Baum

astronomer, L. N. Radlova, using a visual colorimeter with a blue wedge filter, conducted a series of comparative analyses between sunlight and the colours of the planets during 1949. Among other things, it was found that the colour of Mercury and other planets was redder than was to be expected; on the other hand, such an effect was almost negligible in the case of Venus.

The owner of a telescope may find the following hints useful. Mercury appears in easterly elongation in the evening sky with a waning crescent, but with increasing diameter, as it is travelling from superior to inferior conjunction; in westerly elongation, on the other hand, in the morning sky, the crescent waxes, while the diameter decreases, since Mercury is travelling away from the Earth on its path from inferior to superior conjunction. The planet attains its maximum apparent diameter at inferior conjunction, with a value of 12·9 seconds of arc, and its minimum at superior conjunction, with a value of 4·7 seconds. However, in neither instance are we able to see the planet from the Earth, for it is situated in front of (inferior) or behind (superior) the Sun respectively on these occasions. Hence the mean value is approximately 9 seconds of arc. Since our Moon has an apparent diameter of about 1,800 seconds of arc, an astronomer with a good telescope using a magnification of ×200 will see Mercury roughly the same size as the Moon appears to the naked eye.

It is not easy to make out any details on the surface of the planet. In my own experience, a refracting telescope having an aperture of at least four inches is necessary for serious planetary observation (because of the long focal length). But Fauth claims that smaller instruments of, say, three- to four-inch diameter have been known to yield remarkable results.

Practical Observations of Mercury

It is often suggested that the best time to observe Mercury is during the daylight hours, i.e. while the Sun is still above the horizon, since the planet will be higher in the sky during this period, and observation will not be hampered by haze and atmospheric turbulences, which frequently mar observations attempted at dusk or dawn when the planet is close to the horizon. The Greek astronomer, Antoniadi, who did most of his work in France, obtained many excellent results in this manner, although it must be taken into account that he used an instrument of considerable power, the 33-inch refractor at the Meudon Observatory near Paris. Another astronomer who frequently observed Mercury during the day was Giovanni Virginio Schiaparelli (1835–1910). In order to direct the telescope towards the pale disc of the planet during the day, the instrument should be fitted with setting circles. Where these are not fitted, daylight observation is extremely difficult. It should be noted that experience has shown that estimates of the phase made during daytime observations are for the most part too small, despite the use of powerful optics; this is undoubtedly due to the light background. In any case, large telescopes are not necessarily advantageous, since they are far more susceptible to atmospheric turbulences than more modest instruments. However, even for observations at dawn or dusk, much depends on catching the elusive little planet at the right moment; often this is no more than a few minutes.

W. H. Haas in the United States of America sums up his experiences as follows: 'The actual size of the telescope is apparently not the decisive factor. I have myself managed to observe the planet with instruments of various sizes. . . . Filters may help the observer to avoid irradiation of the disc in the lens. But, if success is to be

26

assured, the most important factor is to observe the planet when contrast is at its greatest; surface features can best be seen when the image is not too pale, as during the day, nor too bright, as at dawn or dusk.' The Munich periodical *Mitteilungen für Planetenbeobachter* (*Announcements for Planetary Observers*) makes the following statement in its issue of April–May 1951 : 'Experience over the last few years has shown (1) that colour filters of medium density tone down twilight images of the planet and make for greater accuracy in the observation; (2) that the observation of various features on the disc of Mercury is not necessarily such a very difficult matter.' This latter statement does, however, appear to be something of an exaggeration.

It is as well to remember that there are considerable differences of opinion on this subject, and other astronomers incline to the view that work carried out with small apertures is of dubious value. Moore considers that a telescope of at least 24 inches (for a reflector) is necessary for reliable observations of the surface details (Plate I); he also believes that many of the hard, sharp features recorded with smaller telescopes are due to tricks of the eye instead of actual markings on Mercury itself.

Photography, unfortunately, is of little use in such a connection. It has so far proved impossible to produce anything in the nature of a photographic chart of the planet—and this is understandable when comparison is made with the photographic maps of Mars, which show far less detail even than is visible with a moderate telescope, despite the fact that Mars is closer and larger than Mercury, and may be studied under much better conditions. It would seem, therefore, that space-research methods hold out the only hope of our being able to draw up a really accurate map, and the application of such methods is not likely to take place for some time yet.

However, it may be said that observation of Mercury does offer some reward to the amateur, despite the obvious difficulties. The chief attributes to ensure success —apart, of course, from the use of adequate instruments—are perseverance and self-criticism.

Cf. "Rotation of Mercury" in Sky & Telescope, Vol, xxi, no. 4 [April, 1966], p. 213, which indicates a rotation of 58-59 d based on radar studies. This suggests 58.6462 d as the (siderial) period of rotation — 2/3 of the siderial period of revolution, which would be stable, with small variations.

IV

The Rotation of Mercury

————————————— * —————————————

The rotation period of Mercury, that is to say the 'day' on the planet, was for a long time the subject of some dispute, but, as a result of the work of Antoniadi during the thirties, the problem has now been resolved. The first to detect irregularities in the 'horns' (i.e. the ends of the luminous crescent), as well as some surface detail were Johann Hieronymus Schröter (1745–1816), whose observatory was at Lilienthal near Bremen in Germany, and who was in his day the foremost planetary observer, and his assistant, Karl Ludwig Harding (1765–1836), who later became professor of astronomy at the University of Göttingen in Germany. They carried out their observations at the beginning of the nineteenth century, working during the twilight periods. Since the details they observed did not seem to vary from day to day, they assumed that the Mercurian day must be very similar to our own. Then in 1867 another astronomer, Prince, reached the same conclusion and even calculated the Mercurian days as being 24 hours 05 minutes and 30 seconds.

In 1882, Schiaparelli, who had become famous for his observations of the so-called canals of Mars, began his observations of Mercury in Milan. These he continued until 1889. At first he carried out his observations at dusk,

29

but soon he hit upon the excellent idea of also observing the planet during the day. In this way it became possible for him to observe a particular surface detail on the planet over a period of several hours. During his periods of observation he was, however, unable to detect any marked shift of a particular detail across the disc of the planet, such as would be caused by rotation. This led him to the conclusion that Mercury must have what is called a 'captured rotation', which means that the body turns once on its axis in the same time that it takes to complete one orbit around its primary. Thus the day on Mercury must be equivalent to eighty-eight of our days and the little planet continually keeps the same face towards the Sun, just as the Moon always keeps the same face towards its primary, the Earth. One hemisphere of Mercury, therefore, has continuous day, while the other is in eternal darkness.

This discovery did not at first find universal recognition. Leo Brenner (1857–1928), working in the very favourable climatic conditions of the island of Lussinpiccolo in the Adriatic, off the coast of Dalmatia, thought that he had discovered a rotation period of $33\frac{1}{4}$ hours, but the observations of other astronomers such as Percival Lowell (1855–1916), Jarry-Desloges, Antoniadi, McEwen and, in recent times, Haas all show agreement with Schiaparelli's findings; in addition, this value agrees with the results of spectrographic examinations which have now been undertaken, so that there can no longer be any doubt that the day on Mercury is equal to its year, namely 88 days.

During the last twenty-odd years Bernard Lyot (1897–1952) and later A. Dollfus, working at the Pic du Midi at an altitude of about 9,350 feet above sea level in the Pyrenees, where excellent climatic conditions exist for observation, have shown that Mercury's orbital period and the planet's rotation on its axis coincide to within an accuracy of one part in a thousand.

Undoubtedly, Mercury has a captured rotation for the same reason as the Moon. The second son of Charles Darwin, famous for his theory of evolution, was G. H. Darwin (1845–1912); he was a mathematician, and showed that 'tidal friction' was responsible for the captured rotation of the Moon. In other words, the original rotation was retarded to its present rate through the raising of a tidal mound when the body was still, at least partially, in a plastic state.

The generalization that one hemisphere of Mercury has perpetual day, while the other has eternal night, is not, however, strictly speaking, correct. Mercury's rotation on its axis and its orbital period do not quite keep in time, so that the planet's axis appears to sway slightly, an effect which is known as 'libration'; a similar phenomenon takes place in the case of the Moon. To an observer the libration appears as a slight irregularity in the rotation, particularly if it is a case of captured rotation. On Mercury it occurs because the planet travels faster along its orbit approaching perihelion than towards aphelion (Kepler's second law), while the rotation period remains constant. Owing to the marked eccentricity of Mercury's orbit, the libration effect on this planet is particularly pronounced. Thus one or other limb of the planet is sometimes turned more towards the Sun, the result of which is that there is a zone along the perimeter of the dark half of the planet where the Sun sometimes shines; Haas has estimated the libration on Mercury to amount to 26 per cent. These two narrow wedge-shaped zones are the only regions on Mercury where the Sun rises and sets; so far as the rest of the planet's surface is concerned, the Sun is either permanently up, or it is never seen at all.

The similarities between the rotation conditions of Mercury and our own Moon prompted Max Valier (1895–1930), who, apart from being one of the pioneers of rocketry, was also an astronomer, to describe Mercury as a 'solar moon', a statement which is not without justification.

Closely related to Mercury's axial rotation period is the question of the inclination of its axis, that is to say the angle at which the axis lies relative to the plane of the planet's orbit round the Sun. The usual practice is to indicate not the actual inclination of the axis itself, but rather the inclination of the body's equator, which is, of course, at right-angles to the axis. In the case of the Earth, the equator is inclined at an angle of 23 degrees 27 minutes to the plane of the Earth's orbit; in the case of Mars it is 25 degrees 10 minutes. The tilt of a planet's axis is, by the way, responsible for the changes of season. So far as Mercury is concerned, Schröter estimated the inclination at 20 degrees, and Schiaparelli thought that there was not a great deal of difference between the plane of the planet's equator and the plane of its orbit; according to Haas the inclination is less than 15 degrees, and observers on the Pic du Midi put the value as low as something in the nature of only 7 degrees.

V

Mercury through the Telescope

————————— * —————————

Mercury is a difficult telescopic object; not so much because its disc is only a few seconds of arc in diameter, but mainly because it appears so close to the Sun in the sky. Hence it is hardly surprising that the great William Herschel (1738–1822), who discovered the planet Uranus, was unable to make out any details on the surface of Mercury. The first success in this respect was achieved by Schröter in collaboration with Harding, his assistant, who were, moreover, able to draw up a chart of the features they observed.

First of all, on 26th March 1800, both noticed that the 'horns' of the luminous crescent of Mercury were not alike; the northerly one appeared sharp-pointed, while the southerly one was blunt. On 17th March fourteen years later, a similar effect was recorded by Gruithuisen, and numerous observers have subsequently corroborated this phenomenon. Schiaparelli put it down to the existence of a grey region in the vicinity of the southern horn, and Antoniadi shared his view.

At the time, Schröter also saw in the neighbourhood of Mercury's south pole a light speck which projected above the limb. He assumed that this was due to a high mountain, whose peak was bathed in sunlight, while its base was in the shadow of night. Such an assumption, however, seemed somewhat far-fetched, and was thus never generally accepted, for from the observational data it was not difficult to calculate that the height of this mountain would need to be around 60,000 feet; a mountain of this size on Mercury is, of course, quite unthinkable, when one considers that the highest mountains on the Earth, whose diameter is more than double that of Mercury, are less than half this height. Almost

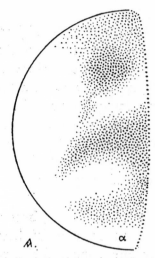

Fig. 6. Drawing of Mercury by
Antoniadi with the Meudon refractor
31st August 1929.

one hundred and forty years later the same phenomenon was again observed, this time by Vaughn on 8th November 1941. The cause is still uncertain; perhaps a refraction effect in such atmosphere as might possibly exist on Mercury, or even a cloud at extreme altitude, though, in view of the evidence, an atmospheric explanation does not sound very plausible.

So far we have mentioned only the deformations of the horns. The first to recognize any detail on the disc of the planet itself was Harding. On 18th May 1801 he detected a dark patch in the southern hemisphere, extending from the limb to the terminator. He saw the same feature again the next day.

During the decade which followed no new features were observed on Mercury. The next astronomer, after Schröter and Harding, who managed to detect a marking on the disc, was Prince; on 11th June 1867 he observed a faint dark mark, again south of the centre of the disc. Then on 13th March 1870 the astronomer Birmingham thought that he had detected a light spot. No further observations were published until Hermann Carl Vogel (1841–1907) issued a report on a longer sequence of observations in the 1870s; he was at that time the director of the Astronomical Observatory at Bothkamp in Holstein, in North Germany.

A new chapter in the study of Mercury opened when Schiaparelli began his observations in 1882. For his work he used the 22 cm. and 49 cm. refractors (8·66 and 19·29 inches respectively) at the Brera Observatory, Milan. The Italian observer described the features to be seen on the planet as being of an extremely delicate nature, not standing out well against their backgrounds. In his opinion the dark markings were of a light browny colour on a dull red background. Using one hundred and fifty individual drawings he was able to compose a general map of the face of the planet, and this, together with that compiled by Antoniadi, remains today as the standard map of Mercury.

At the same time as Schiaparelli, the British amateur astronomer, William Frederick Denning (1848–1931), well known for his painstaking planetary observations, was also working on Mercury. His drawings contain many details; he found them easily discernible and so pronounced that he thought them comparable with those on Mars. The difference in the impressions of these two observers is undoubtedly due to the fact that Schiaparelli used to observe during the day, while Denning preferred the twilight periods. Experience has shown that because of the light background of the sky during the day the contrast on the tiny disc of the planet is considerably reduced, and the rather high magnification used by the Italian emphasized the effect. Furthermore, even that

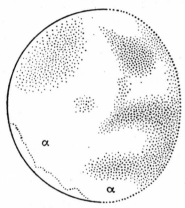

Fig. 7. An earlier Mercury drawing by
Antoniadi, 27th September 1927.

excellent observer, Edward Emerson Barnard (1857–1923) said that with the great Yerkes refractor (102 cm. = 40 in.) the image was sometimes very clear indeed and the patches appeared decidedly dark, comparable with the dark areas on the Moon as seen with the naked eye.

The best map of Mercury available today is certainly that of Antoniadi. From 1924 onwards he observed with the great refractor (83 cm. = 32·68 in.) at the Meudon Observatory near Paris. Using magnifications ranging between ×270 and ×540, Antoniadi worked during daylight. An idea of the power of this instrument may be gathered from the fact that it is able to pick out on Mercury features which are about the same size as the island of Sardinia. A drawing and a chart of Mercury made by Antoniadi are shown in Plate III. The chart is so orientated that it shows the view of the planet at full phase (superior conjunction) and mean libration. The point marked Z then denotes the centre of the day hemisphere, though at maximum libration it may be displaced in longitude to Z' or Z". The names of the various features of the Mercurian landscape are also due to Antoniadi; for the most part he chose names from the legends of Greece and Egypt which had some connection with the god Hermes (Mercury), taking into account the probable arid nature of the planet. On the other hand he also named a bright region on the planet 'Liguria' as a compliment to Schiaparelli, whose homeland south of Turin lay in the ancient province of that name.

After Antoniadi the Pic du Midi became the principal source of news concerning Mercury; here the observers were B. Lyot and A. Dollfus. In the lowlands atmospheric effects tend to reduce contrast, but up in the clear air of the mountain peaks, at an altitude of more than 9,000 feet, where there is less scattered light and the sky is a deep blue, the 23½ in. (60 cm.) refracting telescope was able to yield pictures which were beautifully sharp and contrasty, and it was possible to use magnifications from ×500 to ×800 without undue difficulty. It also proved possible—although not without certain safety pre-cautions—to follow Mercury to as close as two degrees from the Sun. When, on 2nd August 1942, Mercury came into superior conjunction with the unusually great distance of six degrees north of the Sun, Lyot was able to observe the planet from 8th July right through the period of superior conjunction until 13th August without a break. This series of observations not only improved the chart of Mercury, but also provided evidence to show that any mountains which might exist on Mercury could at most be only half as high as the ranges on the Moon. It further proved possible to photograph details on Mercury, as well as measure twenty-three fixed points.

Over the last twenty years W. H. Haas in the United States has studied the planet closely with instruments of various sizes. He also stresses the point that the details on Mercury are reasonably similar to those on Mars, and not so hazy as the alleged markings on Venus; he likens the dark areas with the maria on the Moon. Haas has also compiled a map of Mercury based on his observations; this contains numerous light and dark areas, including those in the vicinity of the terminator (the boundary between the illuminated and dark hemispheres) which have been rather neglected. For this work he also referred to drawings made by a group of observers in the United States.

Finally, during recent years O. C. Ranck in Milton (U.S.A.) has been studying the various features on Mercury and has produced numerous drawings of them, while G. D. Roth in Munich (Germany) has been engaged on trying to improve visual observations of the planet by using strong colour filters.

Mars, lying further from the Sun than does the Earth, shows light areas at its poles, whose extent varies rhythmically with the change of the Martian seasons. We nowadays believe that these polar caps on Mars are composed of a thin blanket of solidified water in some form or other (snow crystals, hoar-frost, or perhaps even a very thin layer of ice). In many respects, therefore, we may liken them to the ice-fields which surround the polar regions on the Earth; on Mercury, on the other hand, a similar phenomenon is lacking. Only Brenner claims that, among other details, he has observed polar caps on Mercury. Haas states that the polar regions on the planet do appear somewhat lighter than the remainder of the disc and that these regions are bordered by a darker rim.

Last, but not least, attention must be drawn to a remarkable similarity which tends to be rather neglected. We know that on Mars the southern hemisphere is predominantly composed of dark regions, while the northern hemisphere consists mainly of light areas; a view of the Earth from space would show a similar effect. If one looks at a map of Mercury, one sees that here too there is a preponderance of dark features in the southern hemisphere. The other planets in the Solar System do not lend themselves for comparisons of this sort, since on Venus, for instance, what we observe from the Earth is not the actual solid surface of the planet, but its covering of atmosphere, while the more distant, larger planets, such as Jupiter, Saturn, Uranus and Neptune, are physically of quite a different nature from their more Earth-like brethren nearer the Sun.

VI

The Surface Features of Mercury

———————— * ————————

Antoniadi listed the various features of the Mercurian surface and the description which follows is based on his work, reading from south to north (see Plate III).

I. WESTERLY ELONGATION
(Morning visibility)

(a) Dark Areas:

1. SOLITUDO PROMITHEI. A grey region near the south pole; roughly equivalent in area to the U.K.; first observed by Denning in 1882; according to Antoniadi it was obscured by cloud in 1928 and 1929; Haas calls it 'South Polar Belt' on the 'Mappa Hermographica' 1936–45; not shown on the map by Schiaparelli.

2. SOLITUDO HERMAE TRISMEGISTI. Adjoins *Solitudo Promithei* to the north; a dark region about the size of Australia; Antoniadi claimed that he never experienced any difficulty in finding it, and that it remained visible even under poor observing conditions; strangely enough it is not mentioned by Schiaparelli, though in my own experience it can be found even with a medium-size instrument; on the west it continues into the *Solitudo Panos*.

3. SOLITUDO MARTIS. Identical with the patch marked 'e' on Schiaparelli's map (Plate VII).

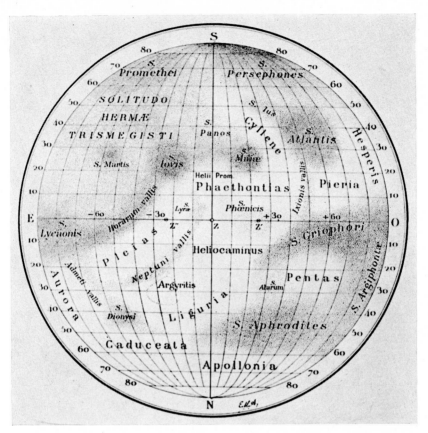

III Map of Mercury by Antoniadi based on his observations of the planet during 1924, 1927, 1928 and 1929 with the 33-inch Meudon refractor

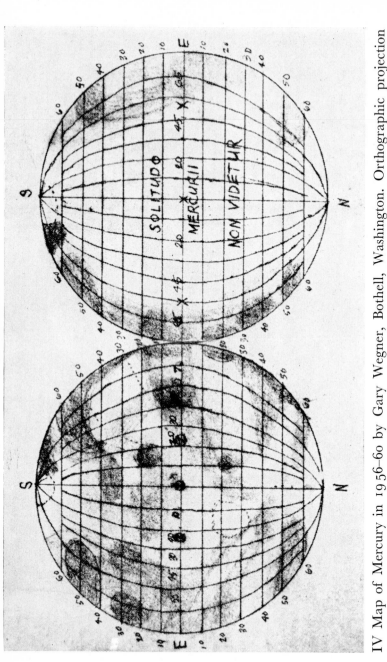

IV Map of Mercury in 1956–60 by Gary Wegner, Bothell, Washington. Orthographic projection of sun-turned (left) and sun-averted (right) hemispheres at mean libration in longitude. Employed 10-inch Cassegrain reflector and other, smaller telescopes. Dashed lines are boundaries of bright areas. The Z's along the equator on the left hemisphere are the limits of the zenithal sun; and the X's along the equator on the right hemisphere are the limits of eternal darkness, according to Wegner. The map thus attempts to depict the libratory zones completely. From *Strolling Astronomer*, Vol. 14,

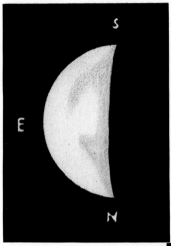

V Drawing of Mercury by J. Escalante (Mexico), 1953 Feb. 27th

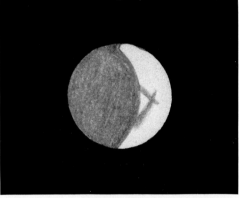

VI Mercury drawing by the author, 1949 Oct. 16th, 5h. 10m. G.M.T.

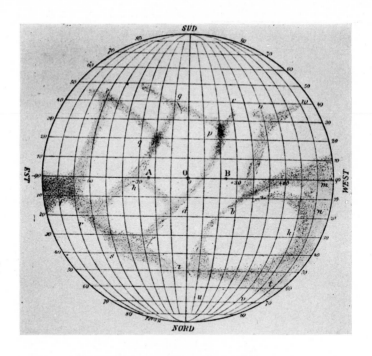

VII Schiaparelli's map of Mercury

VIII Artist's impression of a Mercurian scene

4. SOLITUDO JOVIS. A very dark, round spot; almost always to be seen; first described by Schiaparelli and marked on his map with the letter 'q'.

5. HORARUM VALLIS. A very dark, broad streak; links *Solitudo Lycaonis* with *Solitudo Jovis*; crosses the equator; has been seen by numerous observers; first recorded by Ball and Denning in 1882; designated 'rhq' on Schiaparelli's map; in my own experience it can be detected even with fairly modest instruments.

6. SOLITUDO LYCAONIS. An extremely dark region; about the same size as Great Britain; situated close to the terminator slightly to the north of the equator; appears in the drawings of many observers; decribed by Ball and Denning in 1882; marked 'f' on Schiaparelli's map; can be seen with a medium-size instrument.

7. SOLITUDO LYRAE. A small dark area near the centre of the disc; slightly south of the equator; at the southern end of *Neptuni Vallis*.

8. NEPTUNI VALLIS. A long strip linking *Admeti Vallis* with *Solitudo Lyrae*; perhaps identical to the strip from 's' to 'd' marked on Schiaparelli's map.

9. ADMETI VALLIS. A faint dark band linking *Solitudo Lycaonis* with *Solitudo Dionysi*; probably the same as that marked 'frs' on Schiaparelli's map.

10. SOLITUDO DIONYSI. A dark area about the same size as England; Schiaparelli marks it 's'; according to Antoniadi obscured by local cloud 1927; visible even with relatively small telescopes 1949–52.

11. A 'North Polar Belt' between latitudes +50 and +60 degrees recorded by Haas but not shown on Antoniadi's map; on the contrary, he places the light feature *Caduceata* here.

(b) Light Features:

The light features are confined almost exclusively to the northern hemisphere of the planet.

12. PLEIAS,

13. AURORA,

14. LIGURIA and

15. CADUCEATA do not display any particular characteristics. However, in the centre of *Liguria* there occurs an unusually bright patch, which is known as

16. ARGYRITIS. Denning described it in 1882, and many other observers have also seen it.

II. EASTERLY ELONGATION
(Evening Visibility)

(a) Dark Areas:

17. SOLITUDO PERSEPHONES. An extensive and, for the most part, extremely dark feature, stretching southward from latitude —60 degrees to the pole; called 'South Polar Band' on the map by Haas; Schiaparelli, on whose map the feature is not marked, rightly attributes the occasional blunt appearance of the south horn of the crescent (in contrast to the northern) to the colouring of this region; according to Antoniadi atmospheric phenomena may sometimes be seen here.

18. SOLITUDO IUS is the extension of *Solitudo Atlantis* to the south-east; perhaps identical with the spot near 'a' on the map by Schiaparelli; Haas goes no further than merely marking it on his map.

19. SOLITUDO ATLANTIS. A very dark and extensive feature in the centre of the south-west quadrant; I managed to see it with relatively small telescopes during 1949–56; Schiaparelli shows it noticeably smaller in extent than more recent maps—so much so that Antoni-

adi suggests that considerable changes have taken place in the region.

20. SOLITUDO PANOS. This feature appears only on the chart of Antoniadi, near the central meridian below latitude —40 degrees.

21. SOLITUDO MALAE. Similar to *Solitudo Jovis*; lying below the same latitude on the other side (westerly) of the central meridian; on Schiaparelli's map it is shown as a small but obvious dark patch, marked 'p'; also marked on the map by Haas; Antoniadi noticed temporary obscuration here in 1927.

22. IXIONIS VALLIS. This is a broad band connecting the two dark areas *Solitudo Atlantis* and *Solitudo Criophori*; also marked on Schiaparelli's map and observed by Danjon (Paris) in 1922.

23. SOLITUDO PHOENICIS. A dull spot lying on the equator; also marked on Haas' map.

24. SOLITUDO CRIOPHORI is a very dark and possibly the most obvious feature on this part of the disc of Mercury; almost always visible; on the map by Schiaparelli it stretches from 'b' to 'm'; also marked, of course, on the map by Haas; seen and sketched by numerous observers; in recent years H. Oberndorf (Munich), several other observers and myself have been able to detect this feature with comparative ease using fairly modest instruments. Patrick Moore confirms this.

25. SOLITUDO ARGIPHONTAE. Lies right on the terminator; connects *Solitudo Criophori* with *Solitudo Aphrodites*; marked 'k' on Schiaparelli's map; not shown by Haas even though it can be detected with small instruments.

26. SOLITUDO ALARUM. A dull patch separating the two light areas *Pentas* and *Liguria*; also shown on the map by Haas.

43

27. SOLITUDO APHRODITES. A large dark region extending from latitude +40 to latitude +60 degrees, and from the central meridian to the terminator; seen by numerous observers, even with small instruments; stretches between 'i' and 't' on Schiaparelli's map; Haas marks it in two portions, 'Aphrodites I' and 'Aphrodites II'.

(b) Light Areas:

28. CYLLENE
29. HESPERIS
30. PIERIA
31. PHAETHONTIAS

in the southern hemisphere, and

32. HELIOCAMINUS
33. PENTAS
34. APOLLONIA

in the northern hemisphere.

Recently it has been possible to corroborate the visual observations of Antoniadi by means of photographs. Antoniadi summarizes his experience in the following five points (abridged):

(1) On Mercury, as on Mars, the light areas are more extensive than the dark, and the shape of the latter is, by and large, fairly permanent.

(2) In the light regions there occur some particularly bright patches, just as on Mars and the Moon.

(3) The southern hemisphere of Mercury is more strongly shaded than the northern; such is also the case with the Earth and with Mars.

(4) The grey areas are sometimes bordered by darker rims, as on Mars and the Moon.

(5) The appearance presented by Mercury, like that

of the Earth, Mars and the Moon, tends to show irregular bands.

When one compares the maps of the surface of Mercury which the various observers have compiled, it is noticeable that the drawings made by observers working with smallish instruments are rather hard (i.e. contrasty and well defined), while those produced by observers using more powerful telescopes—quite apart from the greater wealth of detail which such drawings naturally contain—display softer outlines. This difference can already be seen when one compares Schiaparelli's observations with those of Antoniadi, and becomes even more apparent in comparison with more recent drawings of the face of Mercury produced by R. M. Baum (Chester) (Plate II), F. J. Escalante (Mexico) (Plate V), P. Moore (East Grinstead) (Plate I), O. C. Ranck (Milton, U.S.A.), G. D. Roth (Munich) and others. For instance, Moore, using a relatively large reflector, shows the features appreciably less sharp than Baum with a smaller refractor. On the whole, however, the drawings agree to such an extent that there can be no doubt as to the general accuracy of the features portrayed (Plate VI).

Are we then to assume that no changes in the surface details of the planet are to be detected? Is Mercury in fact a completely dead world, such as our Moon, with which the planet displays so definite an affinity?

Here we must differentiate between short-term changes of shorter or longer duration (i.e. more or less seasonal) and long-term changes. Seasonal changes, as for instance the waxing and waning of the polar caps on Mars and Earth, are not to be expected on Mercury. However, Schiaparelli, and later the Fournier brothers and particularly Antoniadi, recorded comparatively frequent temporary changes in the appearance of certain features on Mercury. All these observers have mentioned whitish arcs and bands in the vicinity of the limb of the disc, as well as fading and reappearance of the dark markings, the cycle often taking no more than a few days. Antoniadi in particular recorded numerous instances where individual features have been obscured, an effect which can only really be explained by atmospheric phenomena of some sort (dust storms, for instance).

The Fournier brothers mentioned changes in the brightness of the north polar region, and Antoniadi also remarks that at the time of easterly elongation the northerly pole cap sometimes appears brilliant white, while at others it is merely pale. Even Haas, who has studied these problems extensively, has arrived at the conclusion that, apart from changes in appearance due to the phase and heliocentric position of the planet, occasional temporary changes have definitely been detected; in fact, he differentiates between several types of these, and supports his premises with actual examples. The changes dependent on phase are certainly no more than optical effects; those due to the planet's distance from the Sun (heliocentric distance) could perhaps originate from a marked alteration in the surface temperature of Mercury between perihelion and aphelion.

Besides such temporary changes, Antoniadi definitely believes that a distinct and constant change in the brilliance and dimensions of the feature Atlantis is traceable over the period from 1889 to 1912, and quotes the drawings of a number of expert planetary observers to support his case. From 1882 to 1889 this feature was shown as being small and fairly faint, and triangular in shape; since 1912, on the other hand, it has been depicted by many observers as very large and dark, and shaped as shown on Antoniadi's map.

VII

Has Mercury an Atmosphere?

———————— * ————————

The question of whether Mercury possesses an atmosphere or not, is one which, even to date, has not been fully resolved. During the last century, at any rate, a time when it was hoped to discover in each of the inferior planets a 'second Earth', Mercury was credited with the possession of a dense atmosphere, and further thought on the matter seemed unnecessary. The assumption was based on a number of independent observations, to which we shall return later. Then, in 1871, Vogel examined the spectrum of Mercury; his investigations led him to the conclusion that the spectrum of the planet did not wholly agree with that of the Sun and that the bands resulting from water vapour in the Earth's own atmosphere seemed to be slightly strengthened in the spectrum of Mercury. This was taken to indicate that that planet must be surrounded by an atmosphere containing water vapour. Thus the problem appeared to have been answered. P. Angelo Secchi (1818–1878), who had been the director of the Vatican Observatory in Rome since 1849, wrote in much the same vein in 1871: '. . . that Mercury is enveloped in a dense atmosphere; similarly, the great changes which can be observed on its surface from time to time may be attributed to the formation of clouds.' Even in 1911, J. Riem of the Astronomischen Recheninstitut, Berlin, stated: 'In any case, Mercury

47

possesses an extremely dense atmosphere; so dense, in fact, that we are unable to see through it.'

Nevertheless, after the second half of the nineteenth century, not even such positive assertions could quite allay the doubts as to the actual existence of any appreciable atmosphere on Mercury, and the accuracy of Vogel's spectroscopic investigation was thought to be suspect, particularly as spectroscopy was then still in its infancy so far as astronomy was concerned. The following is a brief summary of the principal objections:

In the years following 1868, Friedrich Zöllner (1834–1882) devoted himself to an intensive photometric study of Mercury, especially with regard to the determination of the planet's albedo. Put briefly, what he says is this: 'Mercury is a body, the nature of whose surface must be very similar to that of the Moon, since like the latter it does not possess any appreciable atmosphere.'

In actual fact, Mercury has the lowest albedo of any of the major planets, almost exactly the same as that of the Moon, which is certainly devoid of any appreciable atmosphere. The table below gives the overall picture.

Planet	Albedo
Mercury	0·07
Venus	0·64
Earth	0·45(?)
Mars	0·15
Jupiter	0·42
Saturn	0·45
Uranus	0·46
Neptune	0·53
Moon	0·073

(For comparison: the albedo of bright cumulus cloud = 0·70)

Moreover, the photometric behaviour of Mercury due to changes in phase shows considerable affinity to that of the Moon, and thus helps to confirm the resemblance between the natures of these two bodies. Observers, for the most part on the Pic du Midi, have also carried out polarization experiments; these again have yielded similar results, for no difference could be found in the light emanating from Mercury and that from the Moon.

In addition, observations of transits of Mercury, while not providing absolutely definite data, would seem to indicate the absence of any but a very tenuous atmosphere on the planet. Mercury and Venus, both of whom have orbits which lie within that of the Earth, must occasionally, as seen from Earth, pass across the face of the Sun. At such times, the observer on Earth sees them as tiny black dots against the background of the bright disc of the Sun. When Venus, which is known to possess an atmosphere which is both dense and fairly deep, passes across the Sun, it is always surrounded by an aureole; this effect is produced by the absorption of light in the atmosphere of the planet. Most of the observers of transits of Mercury, however, have been unable to detect such an effect, a fact which again points to the absence of any appreciable atmosphere. Herschel remarks that during a transit of Mercury he saw the planet as a sharply defined spot without any trace of an aureole. I myself was able to observe the transit of Mercury on 14th November 1953 under ideal weather conditions at the observatory in Madrid, and failed to notice any phenomenon of this sort, and Moore in England had a similar experience. On the other hand, a negative result of this kind is, in itself, no proof.

Especially impressive arguments against Mercury having anything more than a very tenuous atmosphere can be put forward on purely theoretical grounds. Mercury is the least massive of all the major planets; gravitational attraction and hence also escape velocity at the surface of the planet are low. Therefore, in view of the exceedingly high day temperatures, the planet would be unable to hold on to the molecules of the gases comprising its atmosphere, since these would for the most part be moving at speeds faster than the escape velocity. There is a great number of astronomers, who even go so far as to maintain that Mercury has failed to retain any of its atmosphere.

However, one must not forget that there is also some not inconsiderable evidence pointing to the existence of a very tenuous atmospheric mantle around Mercury. After the end of World War II, Haas in the U.S.A. in particular has been engaged upon, as he puts it, gathering irrefutable evidence to show that there is an atmosphere on Mercury.

Haas admits that the theoretical arguments ranged against the belief that Mercury possesses an atmosphere are very strong. Thus they require detailed contradiction both through observation and through theory, but he hopes to be able to furnish the necessary proof.

Even Schröter claims that he had repeatedly detected clouds on Mercury, in fact 'obscuration' as well as clearing. Three-quarters of a century later, Schiaparelli stated that the spots on Mercury's surface appeared clearer the closer they were to the centre of the disc, and that the closer they were to the edge of the disc the paler they looked. He believed that such an effect could really only be explained by assuming the existence of an atmosphere. He even went so far as to consider this atmosphere to be suitable for the formation of clouds, and, moreover, that it was probably more akin to our terrestrial air than to the atmosphere on Mars. Even so reliable an astronomer as Antoniadi frequently mentions dust-storms and obscurations, 'immense pallid clouds on the planet which often obscured the features' ('Nuées blafardes immenses de la planète, qui éclipsent souvent ses taches'), and 'their rapid changes' ('leurs changements rapides'); he mentions many instances and supports these with drawings which he made at the 33-inch refractor at Meudon. As a result of perspective the cloud haze becomes more conspicuous towards the edge of the disc. On 11th April 1931, Quénisset at the Flammarion Observatory, at Juvisy near Paris, even managed to photograph such a cloud in the region of Solitudo Criophori. Since the albedo of these cloud-like hazes is exceedingly small, and is in no way comparable with the albedo of terrestrial cloud formations, Antoniadi considered that they must be clouds of very fine dust stirred up in the thin atmosphere. On this point Haas writes: '. . . The large difference in temperature between opposite sides of the terminator must cause strong winds to blow across this boundary. If the surface material is finely divided, and the great range in temperature to which the Mercurian rocks are subject should pulverize them through differential expansion, such winds would raise clouds of dust that would dim the incoming sunlight.'*

In the case of Mercury, observations of the phase provide us with no definite clue either as to the presence or the absence of an atmosphere on the planet. Nevertheless, observers even during the nineteenth century—the first probably being Fritsch in 1802—noticed numerous differences between the predicted and the observed phase, and Brenner claimed that deviations of

Popular Astronomy, Vol. LV, No. 3, March 1947.

up to nine days could occur between the commencement of dichotomy and the time predicted for this. Dichotomy is a term used in connection with the two inner planets, Mercury and Venus, to indicate that their phase is exactly half, i.e. equivalent to Moon at the first or last quarter. Haas also lays great stress on the importance of determining the angle of phase, and in 1935 observations of this led McEwen to the conclusion that the depth of the Mercurian atmosphere must be in the nature of at least 120 miles. In my own experience, Mercury does not really lend itself for using observations of this kind to assess the extent of its atmospheric mantle, since observational conditions are far from favourable and the findings are too dependent on the time of day when the observation is made as well as the size of the instrument being used.

On the other hand, according to Haas, deformations of the terminator, such as those observed by Fournier in 1909–10, do indicate the presence of an atmosphere.

In contrast to the observations mentioned earlier, there are occasionally reports of an aureole being seen around the disc of the planet during a transit. On the occasion of the transit of Mercury of 8th May 1924, whose end, in the early hours of the morning, was visible in Europe, Futschek and Severinski, using the 8-inch refractor at the Urania Observatory, Vienna, claimed that they had detected an aureole surrounding Mercury.

Finally, that experienced planetary observer K. Novák (1887–1958) in Prague reported that he had observed the disc of the planet surrounded by a delicate ring of light, which he estimated to have a width of about one second of arc. This was on 14th April 1944, two days after the greatest easterly elongation (Mercury in the night sky), when he was using his Zeiss refractor with magnifications of ×132 and ×183. This corresponds with a claim made by Brenner, who reported in 1896 that he had observed the night hemisphere of Mercury surrounded by an aureole.

It can be seen, therefore, that the evidence relating to the existence of an atmosphere on Mercury is by no means definite, either for or against. We can be certain, however, that a dense atmosphere of the kind that astronomers of the nineteenth century took for granted, could not be present on the planet. On the other hand, we must accept the fact that there probably exists a very tenuous atmosphere. This would explain the formation of hazy patches and other types of observed phenomena. Moreover, in recent times A. Dollfus at the Pic du Midi has pointed out that the simplest explanation for certain differences obtained in polarization measurements, would be the assumption that a very thin atmosphere exists on Mercury.

Finally, in this connection, there is yet another phenomenon which must be mentioned. On Venus, which like Mercury also shows phases, occasionally (admittedly not very often), when the crescent is thin, the unilluminated portion of the disc appears suffused with a very faint shimmer of light. Schröter was the first to observe this 'Ashen Light', which is reminiscent of the 'earthshine' on the Moon, which occurs shortly after or just before new moon, even though the cause for this effect on Venus is due to quite different reasons. On Venus the origin probably lies in something of the nature of aurorae, while in the case of the Moon the effect is certainly the result of sunlight reflected from the Earth. It has not yet been determined whether Mercury is subject to similar phenomena; indeed, owing to the adverse viewing conditions, it will be extremely difficult to establish with any degree of certainty. Brenner claimed to have seen such an effect on Mercury in 1896, and Novák's observation of 1944, mentioned above, could also be interpreted in the same sense.

A recent study made by the Russian astronomer N. A. Kozirev is of interest in connection with the problem of the hypothetical atmosphere of Mercury. Kozirev's results are only tentative as yet, but are certainly worth describing here.

As we have seen, Mercury is never visible against a dark background except when it is low down in the sky. In such circumstances the viewing conditions are always atrocious, and it has been said that there is very little point in looking at the planet through a telescope when it is visible to the naked eye—though this point of view, expressed by Moore, may be too extreme. This means that if Mercury is to be seen when high up, observations must be conducted in daylight, when the presence of the Sun makes the sky inconveniently bright. (The same thing also applies to Venus, but to a lesser degree, and in any case a bright background is useful in reducing the glare from Venus' cloud-covered disc.)

There is, however, one exception to this rule. On the rare occasion of a total solar eclipse, the Sun is covered by the Moon, and the sky becomes so dark that stars are visible without optical aid. Only then may Mercury be observed against a dark background and at a convenient altitude.

Eclipse expeditions make up an important part of modern astronomical research, and the results obtained from them have yielded a tremendous amount of information about the Sun's chromosphere and corona— as well as leading to other investigations, such as the confirmation of the relativity theory by observations of the apparent displacements of stars in the vicinity of the eclipsed Sun. Not until 1961, however, was a solar eclipse used for carrying out studies directly related to Mercury.

The eclipse of February 1961 was well seen over much of Europe. Starting in the western part of the continent, the track extended over Southern France, North Italy, Jugoslavia and the Crimea; in Britain the eclipse was partial (though cloud unfortunately covered most of the British Isles). Three of Europe's major observatories lay in the track of totality—St. Michel in France, Arcetri in Italy and the Crimean Astrophysical Observatory in the U.S.S.R. Weather conditions were generally good, and some excellent results were obtained.

In the Crimea, Kozirev decided to ignore the main spectacle of the eclipse and to spend the time of totality in making spectrographic and polarimetric observations of Mercury in a new attempt to confirm the presence of an atmosphere. This meant that he did not see the eclipse at all, which must have been a considerable sacrifice in view of the fact that a total eclipse is the grandest sight in all nature. However, it was an opportunity not to be missed, since it will be a very long time before a major European observatory is again crossed by the track of totality.

Kozirev was favoured with excellent conditions, and was able to carry through his full programme. A first analysis of the results shows that they were wholly negative, and that no trace of an atmosphere round Mercury was detected. The whole question must therefore be regarded as completely open still, and we must await further information before it is possible to come to a definite conclusion one way or the other.

If Mercury does indeed prove to be devoid of an appreciable atmosphere, as many authorities now believe, we must reject the 'obscurations' claimed by Antoniadi and others, for it is difficult to see how any such obscuration could persist for any length of time in the absence of atmosphere. It must also be agreed that the obscurations themselves are, in any case, so difficult to see, that grave doubts attach to them, and Antoniadi's statement that they are 'more frequent and obliterating than those of Mars' is not in accord with more modern results.

At best, the atmosphere on Mercury must be painfully thin—much too tenuous to support living organisms of any kind known to us on Earth. Dollfus' figure for the density, one-threehundredth of that of the Earth's air at sea level, may well prove to be a considerable overestimate. Summing up, it is wisest to say that, although Mercury may possibly have traces of an atmosphere, it should, for most purposes, be regarded as an airless world.*

* Cf. Kozyrev, Nikolai A., "The Atmosphere of Mercury," in *Sky & Telescope*, vol. xxvii, no.6 [June 1964], pp.339-341. Cf. also *Ibid.*, vol. xxx, no.6 [Dec. 1965], p. 360 on this subject.

VIII

The Surface Temperature of Mercury

———————————— * ————————————

The mean distance of Mercury from its primary is only about four-tenths the distance which the Earth is from the Sun. Consequently Mercury is subject to six and a half times more light and heat from the Sun than is the Earth. This, however, is only a mean value, for the considerable eccentricity of the orbit of Mercury means that the amount of radiation which the planet receives varies greatly: at perihelion Mercury receives more than ten times the amount of radiation, and at aphelion—six weeks later—'only' four and a half times the radiation which the Earth receives from the Sun. Thus, the average temperature must be greater than on the Earth.

However, since Mercury has a captured rotation, the temperature in the day hemisphere is bound to rise to an extremely high level. In contrast, the night hemisphere only receives weak radiation from space, and as a result is subject to very low temperatures.

In addition, these conditions are made far more absolute owing to the absence of any marked atmosphere; on Earth the atmosphere helps to even out the temperature distribution. This fact is borne out by experiments with thermocouples, such as those which have been carried out since 1923–4 by Pettit and Nicolson with the 100-inch Hooker telescope at the Mount Wilson Observatory. It was found that the temperature on the day hemisphere of Mercury can rise to as high as +400 degrees Centigrade (+752° F.), while on the night side it almost certainly sinks to below −100 degrees Centigrade (−148° F.).

In recent times, W. M. Sinton of the Lowell Observatory (U.S.A.) and J. Strong of John Hopkins University (U.S.A.) have revised the temperature measurements of all the planets from Mercury to Uranus inclusive. One of their findings was that when the Sun is directly overhead the surface temperature on Mercury rises to +337 degrees Centigrade (+638° F.).

The problem of the surface temperature of Mercury has recently been re-examined by J. C. G. Walker, who used as a basis for his deliberations not only known data, but also factors such as the probable chemical composition and internal structure of the planet. Walker estimates that the temperature in the night hemisphere is −245° C. (approx. −410° F.). On the day hemisphere, where the Sun is at the zenith, he considers the mean temperature to be as high as +348° C. (approx. +660° F.). Moreover, even in those regions where the sun is at an altitude of 45° above the horizon the surface temperature of Mercury is still in the region of +300° C. (approx. 570° F.), while in those regions where the altitude of the sun is 12° the temperature, according to Walker, is +150° C. (approx. 300° F.); on the terminator, however, there is an abrupt drop in the surface temperature of the planet.

IX

The Mercurian Landscape

————————————— * —————————————

So far as future space flights are concerned, a landing on Mercury will not offer the travellers in space a great deal of prospect. Nevertheless, it is interesting to speculate on the nature of this little world, if only from the academic point of view. What then awaits the intrepid astronaut when he reaches Mercury?

The first thing one would notice is that the visual horizon, provided that no mountains obstruct the view, will seem much closer than the observer is used to from his experience on Earth. Next, one would become physically aware of the fact that one did not weigh as much as back on Earth. The first is due to the fact that Mercury has a smaller diameter than the Earth, and hence the planet's surface curves more sharply. The second is due to the smaller mass of Mercury, and the less pronounced gravitational attraction. Therefore, apart from the impediment of protective suits and respiratory equipment, the space traveller would be capable of greater physical feats than on his home planet. One would be able to travel on foot over far greater distances without undue exhaustion; jump higher and further; using the same amount of force, one could throw a stone further, and then have the experience of seeing it fall silently to the ground, for the very thin atmosphere is virtually incapable of propagating sound waves.

The Mercurian Landscape

There is good reason to assume that the landscape on Mercury is very similar to that on the Moon. The resemblance can already be seen in the dimensions of the two bodies. In size Mercury lies about halfway between Mars and the Moon, in fact the dimensions of Mercury come closer to those of the Moon than those of any of the other planets.

	Diameter	*Mass* (Earth$=1$)
Mars	4,200 miles	0·107
Mercury	3,000 miles	0·055
Moon	2,160 miles	0·0123

Even in its physical nature Mercury lies somewhere between Mars and the Moon, closer to the latter than the former. We are able to obtain a good idea of the rocks present on the surface of a distant planet by means of polarization and photometric experiments, as well as the albedo. The following list is of interest in this connection:

Albedo Values for a Number of Terrestrial Substances

	Albedo	*Colour*
Chalk	0·85	White
Pumice	0·48	Bluish-white
Limestone	0·36	Whitish-grey
Granite	0·31	Reddish-grey
Clay	0·2	Yellowish-grey
Volcanic ash (Vesuvius)	0·16	Bluish-grey
Alluvium	0·14	Yellowish-brown
Quartz porphyry	0·09	Reddish-brown
Obsidian	0·08	Blue-black
Basalt	0·05	Dark grey
Lava from Mt. Etna	0·04	Dark grey

Another respect in which Mercury resembles the Moon is that there are not likely to be any seas or oceans; we have good reason for assuming that the bright markings on the surface of the planet do in fact represent mountainous regions, while the dark areas are extensive plains, rather like those of the Moon as seen with the naked eye. Mercury is bound to have some mountain ranges, even though they might not be of quite such an extreme height as Schröter once claimed.

From the albedo of the planet we learn that dark rocks must predominate on the surface. Just as on the Moon, the surface of Mercury is probably covered with volcanic (and igneous) rock, while sedimentary rocks are likely to be altogether lacking. As a result of his photometric investigations, the French astronomer B. Lyot has come to the conclusion that vast areas of Mercury's surface must be covered with volcanic ash. Whether there is still any volcanic activity on the planet remains doubtful, however, though it cannot be entirely excluded. Certain phenomena claimed to have been observed during transits of the planet, which earlier astronomers thought to be due to volcanic outbursts, are nowadays largely discredited.

Even though the surface of Mercury is unlikely to have been shaped by the agency of water, we may be sure that another equally powerful force has certainly taken a hand, namely the intense heat of the nearby Sun. This is particularly so in the vicinity of the terminator, where, as a result of Mercury's considerable libration, there occurs a definite change between day and night conditions: the violent heating of the dark rocks on exposure to the intense sunlight, and the subsequent rapid cooling so soon as the Sun sinks below the horizon once more, must certainly have brought about a breakdown of the rock substance. A similar kind of erosion, though to a much lesser degree, occurs in desert areas in the tropics and subtropics on the Earth. Even the continual bombardment by tiny cosmic bodies (meteorites), to which the surface of Mercury is subjected in consequence of its inadequate atmospheric shield, is eminently likely to have played its part in decomposing the original rock masses.

One may therefore rightly assume that the vast plains are in fact sun-drenched deserts, covered by a layer of fine dust and grit.

At the present time it is impossible to give a really accurate picture, simply because we still have no definite proof of whether or not there is a tenuous atmosphere. Antoniadi, who believed in the presence of obscurations, believed that an atmosphere—of a sort—existed, and made an exhaustive theoretical study of it. His conclusions are given below, but it must be remembered that much of what he says will be rendered invalid if Mercury proves to be virtually airless (as now seems to be the general view).

However, as yet the question remains open, so let us see what Antoniadi has to say about conditions on this strange, hostile little world.

Even though the atmosphere on Mercury can be no more than extremely tenuous, dust-clouds and dust-storms are by no means rarities on the planet. In comparison the worst *simoom* of the Sahara Desert would seem like a refreshing sea-breeze. There may even be dust-spouts.

Antoniadi made a particular study of the circulatory system of the Mercurian atmosphere. The diagram on page 63 showing how these great air streams arise has been taken from his paper on the subject.

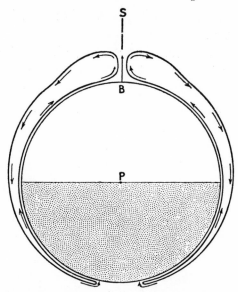

Fig. 8. Diagram to show Antoniadi's conception of the overall circulatory system of Mercury's atmosphere. It represents a section through the globe of Mercury; the upper half (white) has perpetual day, while the lower half (shaded) has eternal night. The Sun shines from the direction of S, and thus B on the surface is that point where the Sun is directly overhead.

The atmosphere on Mercury is heated by the Sun, expands, rises and spreads towards the un-illuminated hemisphere. In the process it cools and sinks, flowing back into the day hemisphere along the surface of the planet as a cold air-stream.

Where the Sun is at the zenith, i.e. at the centre of the illuminated hemisphere, the intense heat sets up convection currents in the atmosphere; these may well be extremely violent. At high altitude the heated air begins to flow outwards from the centre of convection, streaming over the terminator into the night hemisphere; meanwhile cold masses of air are drawn along the surface of the planet from the night hemisphere towards the centre of convection, thus causing intensely cold winds to sweep across the terminator.

Even if one assumes that the overall circulatory system in the Mercurian atmosphere follows this pattern, there is no reason, in Antoniadi's opinion, why local winds should not also arise. The cause of these would be temperature differences between light and dark areas of the surface, between mountains and low-lying plains, which would result in a local distribution of what atmosphere there was and so bring about winds. Antoniadi was of the opinion that these would be fast-moving owing to the proximity of the Sun, and further that they would be more powerful during perihelion than at aphelion. He felt that such occurrences on the planet fully fitted in with his observations.

Camille Flammarion (1842–1925), the great French astronomer, considered that nature could take many forms according to circumstances and environment, and from this he concluded that Mercury need not be entirely lifeless; others also have suggested that a very low type of life, say in the form of microbes, could possibly subsist in the polar regions, though in view of the physical conditions obtaining on the planet, all these suggestions now seem to be highly improbable. Owing to the extremes of temperature, the lack of water and the almost complete lack of an atmosphere the chemical composition of which we do not know, and the unfavourable rotation period, we must perforce assume that any form of plant or animal life, let alone advanced life, is quite out of the question. Even future space-travellers from our planet will have to avail themselves of all their scientific and technical knowledge merely for brief residence in the inhospitable world of Mercury.

X

The Sky as seen from Mercury

———————————— * ————————————

Having landed on Mercury and taken note of the strange environment, we would next turn our attention towards the sky.

The general appearance of the sky on Mercury will, of course, be largely determined by the almost total lack of atmosphere. In consequence, even on the day side, the sky would not appear the blue colour to which we are accustomed; instead it would look dark, nearly black, similar to the sky as seen by airmen flying at great heights. In some respects the lack of atmosphere would make Mercury a suitable location for an astronomical observatory; the drawback on the Earth is that the astronomer is at the mercy of the whims of the weather, the turbulence of the air, and the diffusion and absorption of cosmic radiations.

Owing to the lack of all but perhaps a very tenuous atmosphere on Mercury, none of the phenomena which on Earth have their origin in the atmosphere would occur. Lack of water on Mercury means that there could be neither cumulus clouds, composed of water droplets, nor fleecy or wispy clouds, composed of ice crystals. Thus it could never snow or rain; rainbows would not occur, neither would aureoles round the Sun, nor haloes, double suns, or shafts of sunlight, and probably, despite the glowing heat, there would be no

E

such phenomena as the 'Fata Morgana' and similar illusions.

In the day hemisphere of Mercury, the unusual size of the Sun would catch one's attention immediately. Seen from the Earth, the apparent diameter of the solar disc has a mean value of 32 minutes of arc, i.e. slightly more than half a degree. But to an observer on Mercury—when the planet is at mean distance from the Sun—the solar disc would appear 83 minutes of arc in diameter. Naturally, the apparent size of the Sun varies with the distance from it. The eccentricity of the Earth's orbit is not sufficiently marked for there to be much difference between the apparent diameter of the Sun at perihelion and at aphelion; in fact the values are respectively 33 and 31 minutes of arc. In the case of Mercury, however, which has a highly pronounced orbital eccentricity, the apparent diameter of the solar disc is 68 minutes of arc at aphelion and 104 minutes at perihelion. It would therefore be possible to observe many sunspots without the aid of telescopes.

In those regions of the day hemisphere which border on the terminator, and where the Sun is not far above the horizon, it will still look like a perfectly circular disc; on the Earth we normally experience a distorted vision of the Sun in such conditions, due to the fact that the light rays from the Sun strike the Earth's atmosphere obliquely, thus producing the impression of slight flattening.

While on the Earth solar coronagraph stations have to be situated on the tops of high mountains in order to avoid scattered light in the atmosphere as much as possible, this would be an unnecessary precaution on Mercury, where a possible atmosphere would in any case be extremely thin. For the same reason at any rate the brighter stars and planets will be visible even during the day; most brilliant of all, of course, Venus, which during opposition comes as close as 24 million miles. In actual fact Venus will remain visible from Mercury even fairly close to the Sun. From Mercury one would also be able to see the Earth without any great difficulty, even in full sunshine, and likewise, though to a lesser degree, Mars, Jupiter and Saturn.

From the night hemisphere of Mercury one would enjoy a truly splendid view of the heavens. The familiar constellations would be in their accustomed places, but the stars which compose them would shine with a steady light; they would not appear to flicker. With the naked eye one would be able to see not only more stars than are visible from Earth, but also fainter ones, because some of the light from the stars is absorbed in the Earth's atmosphere. The Milky Way will thus provide a glorious sight. More astonishing perhaps will be the slowness of the procession of the constellations across the Mercurian sky. A star may take twelve hours to cross the Earth's sky, but as seen from Mercury it will take 44 of our days, since the sidereal day on Mercury is equal to 44 terrestrial days.

The brightest object in Mercury's night sky will be Venus, which, like all the other planets in our system, can enter into opposition to the Sun as seen from Mercury, as this is the innermost of them all. At such times Venus is bright enough to cast distinct shadows on Mercury; in fact, the apparent size of the disc of Venus on these occasions, as seen from Mercury, can be as much as 70 seconds of arc. This maximum occurs when conditions are particularly favourable, i.e. if the opposition occurs when Mercury is at aphelion. Even light from the Earth is likely to cast shadows on Mercury, but, needless to say, the Earth will not appear nearly so bright as Venus. In the Mercurian night sky, the apparent diameter of the Earth can become as large as 33 seconds of arc, and together with its companion the Moon must constitute a fine double. The red planet Mars has a brilliance of something slightly less than second magnitude, and Jupiter and Saturn, despite the fact that they may attain first magnitude, are nevertheless not so bright as they appear from Earth. On the other hand, Uranus, which from the Earth is only barely discernible with the naked eye, would be visible from Mercury without the aid of a telescope.

On this near neighbour of the Sun comets will provide an unusually fine spectacle, for, from this vantage point, they are seen to develop a brilliance and a tail of such length as are only rarely observed on some of the larger comets from the Earth. 'Shooting stars' will glow but very briefly in the thin Mercurian atmosphere, since the mean orbital velocity of the planet is 29·8 miles per second (Earth = 18·6 miles per second), and moreover the meteoric particles themselves are travelling faster at this close proximity to the central body of the Solar System than they do at the distance of the Earth. In any case, falls of meteorites are only to be expected on the surface of Mercury, since the tenuous atmosphere must be a poor protection against the cosmic bombardment.

A pronounced feature of the Mercurian sky will be Zodiacal Light, which on the Earth can really be seen well only in the tropics. Mercury, in contrast, is actually within this cloud of matter surrounding the Sun, and it is this cloud of matter, shaped like a double-convex lens, which is the origin of Zodiacal Light. This manifests itself as a faint but broad band of light across the whole sky along the plane of the Sun's equator, being slightly brighter in the direction opposed to that of the Sun (corresponding to opposition in the terrestrial sky).

It is possible that Mercury is also subject to intense and frequent aurorae, and hence also violent magnetic storms. Owing to the planet's proximity to the Sun these will take place within a matter of only twelve hours after the beginning of the solar eruption responsible for the phenomenon. Thus Mercury would be an interesting study from the geophysical—perhaps 'Hermophysical' would be more appropriate—point of view.

Lastly, of course, there is the fact that Mercury is not accompanied by a satellite in its journey round the Sun, for, apart from distant Pluto, about which we know so little, Mercury and Venus, the two inferior planets, are the only major planets of the Solar System which do not have at least one satellite. If Mercury were, in fact, accompanied by a satellite, this would normally not be an easy object to find, in view of the fact that Mercury is itself such a difficult body to observe. Any satellite of the planet would naturally be much smaller than its primary, and, seen through a telescope, show the same phase. On the other hand, it would prove considerably easier to detect such a moon during a transit of Mercury, when the planet shows as a small dark spot on the bright face of the Sun. On such occasions the satellite would manifest itself as a second black spot keeping pace with the planet throughout the transit. However, although 44 transits of Mercury have taken place since 1631, no reliable sighting of such a phenomenon has ever been made.

XI

Beyond Mercury — Vulcan?

———————————— * ————————————

Until the year 1781, astronomers knew of only six planets, or wandering stars. These were Mercury, Venus, Earth, Mars, Jupiter and Saturn. Then on 13th March 1781, Herschel discovered that there was another planet further from the Sun than Saturn, namely Uranus. From perturbations in the orbit of Uranus, an Englishman, John Couch Adams (1819–1892), and a Frenchman, Urbain Jean Joseph Leverrier (1811–1877), working independently, deduced that there was yet another planet even further from the Sun; this planet was subsequently found on the evening of 23rd September 1846 by Johann Gottfried Galle (1812–1910), and the new planet was named Neptune. Finally in 1930, the even more distant planet Pluto was added to the list, and there are some astronomers who believe in the existence of a 'trans-Plutonian' member of the Solar System. Just as the limits of the Solar System have gradually been pushed outwards, the question arises whether Mercury is, in fact, the innermost planet of the system, closest to the Sun.

Since any planet having an orbit within that of Mercury would be very close to the Sun indeed, and is unlikely to be larger than Mercury, it would require exceptionally favourable viewing conditions to see such a planet either with the naked eye or with a telescope.

It is the powerful gravitational attraction exercised by the Sun which holds all the planets in their orbits, and makes them travel around the centre of gravity of the system. But the individual planets also exert mutual attractions on each other, because gravity is an intrinsic characteristic of matter, and every mass exerts a gravitational pull on every other mass. For this reason perturbations, or irregularities, occur in the orbits of the planets, and such perturbations can be calculated mathematically. For the most part they are expressed in the fact that the 'longitude of perihelion', i.e. the

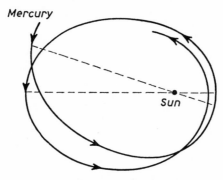

Fig. 9. The motion of Mercury's perihelion.

direction from the Sun to the point of the orbit of a given planet nearest to the Sun, undergoes what is called a precession; in other words, it moves forward along the orbit. After two centuries of accurate observation, these values are known. Now, it has been found that in the case of Mercury this precession has speeded up by 40 seconds of arc over a period of one hundred years; according to the laws of gravity, such a thing should not happen. What then is the reason for this strange behaviour?

Leverrier, who already extended the known outer limits of the Solar System by helping to establish the existence of the planet Neptune, believed, having taken into account all possible causes for such perturbation, that the only feasible explanation was the assumption of an intra-Mercurian planet. He first put this suggestion forward in 1859 in a letter to his compatriot, Hervé Faye (1814–1902). In fact, he was so convinced as to the accuracy of his assumption that he even gave this hypothetical planet the name Vulcan, and later tried to calculate its orbit.

The viewing conditions for Mercury are already difficult enough but an intra-Mercurian planet would become optically accessible on only two occasions: first as a small black dot moving across the face of the Sun when it comes directly between the latter and the Earth, and secondly, as a star-like body not far from the Sun during a total solar eclipse, provided that the planet happened to be at maximum elongation at the time.

The first seemed to offer the best chances of discovery, so Leverrier searched through records of earlier observations for reference to relatively fast-moving spots on the face of the Sun. Eventually he found records of a total of twenty-eight such observations made between 1761 and 1876. In particular one observation by a French doctor and amateur astronomer, Lescarbault, made on 26th March 1859 struck him as being significant. It would take too long to enter into a discussion as to the veracity or otherwise of each of these observations individually, especially as we are now certain that they could not possibly refer to an intra-Mercurian planet. This, of course, leaves open the question of what, in fact, these observations might have been; possibly small round sunspots; perhaps even high-flying birds.

At one time it almost seemed as if a search in the immediate vicinity of the Sun during a total eclipse were to furnish the desired results. In Ann Arbor, U.S.A., Watson, known for his discoveries of asteroids, noticed an object of the fourth magnitude near the Sun during the eclipse of 29th July 1878, which happened to be total in that part of North America. He was under the impression that this object did not coincide with the position of any known star. Unfortunately, it was found later that in his haste, necessitated by the brief duration of totality, he must have made an error. During subsequent total eclipses the vicinity of the Sun has been thoroughly checked photographically with the best available optical equipment, but so far without success.

It has since become generally accepted that there is no major planet orbiting the Sun closer than Mercury. Nevertheless, among those who claimed that they had observed what they thought to be the intra-Mercurian planet, in front of the Sun, there were several very experienced observers, and it seems strange that they should all have been mistaken. It has been suggested that in some instances an asteroid with an unusual orbit—as, for example, Apollo, Adonis, Hermes, or even Icarus— whose perihelion lies within the compass of the orbit of the Earth, happened to be passing close to our planet, between the latter and the Sun; or that a large meteoric body might have been the cause. These explanations, however, do not appear very probable, and it has been calculated that even a relatively large asteroid (say, 25 miles in diameter) would normally remain quite invisible during a transit, with our present optical equipment, because of its small apparent diameter. This argument also applies to a meteoric body—in fact, there seems to be no basic difference between a large meteorite and a junior member of the asteroid swarm.

It is thus safe to assume that Vulcan is a myth, and that Mercury is actually the closest-in of the Sun's family of planets.

XII

A World of Extremes

———————————— * ————————————

Mercury is the nearest of the major planets to the Sun; apart from meteoric bodies, only one or two comets and the asteroid Icarus (whose perihelion lies within the orbit of Mercury, while its aphelion lies out beyond the orbit of Mars) approach more closely to the Sun. This means that Mercury enjoys the shortest light period (the time taken by light from the Sun to reach the planet in question), as well as having the shortest orbital distance to travel. Seen from Mercury all the other planets are superior and none will come into inferior conjunction with the Sun.

Apart from Pluto, the orbit of Mercury shows the greatest eccentricity; and, again apart from Pluto, the greatest inclination to the plane of the ecliptic. The orbital period of Mercury is the least, and the orbital velocity the greatest in the Solar System.

Mercury has the smallest diameter of all the major planets, the smallest surface area, the smallest volume and also the smallest mass. Gravitational acceleration at the surface of Mercury is the least of all the planets, but its density is probably the greatest—its only really close rival being our own Earth. With the exception of Venus, it is the only planet which does not show appreciable flattening at the poles, polar compression.

It is the only planet with a captured rotation, as a

result of which it has the longest rotation period, as well as the longest sidereal day in the Solar System. In contrast to its brothers and sisters in the system, its 'seasons' are brought about not only as the result of axial inclination, but also through a marked libration in longitude, and the marked eccentricity of its orbit.

Mercury receives a greater intensity of light and heat from the Sun than any other planet. It is at once the hottest and the coldest planet; the temperature on the equator in the day hemisphere is the highest in the Solar System, while the night hemisphere, which is permanently turned away from the Sun, boasts the lowest temperature.

Mercury also has a lower albedo than any other planet. In his report to the Paris Academy in 1950, A. Danjon even puts it as low as 0·055.

Furthermore, Mercury and Venus are the only planets which do not possess at least one satellite—we do not count Pluto, because we know so little about it.

XIII

Transits of Mercury

————————— * —————————

The two planets whose orbits lie within that of the Earth will from time to time pass in front of the Sun as seen from the Earth. On these occasions Mercury or Venus will show up as a black dot against the bright face of the Sun. Phenomena of this sort are known as transits.

As has already been mentioned, the plane of Mercury's orbit is inclined at an angle of 7 degrees to the plane of the ecliptic. The points where the orbit of Mercury crosses the plane of the ecliptic are known as the nodes. In view of its short orbital period, Mercury often passes between the Sun and the Earth (inferior conjunction); but due to the inclination of its orbit, the planet usually passes either above or below the Sun as seen from the Earth. A transit will occur only when Mercury happens to be very near a node during inferior conjunction. The longitude of the ascending node of Mercury's orbit corresponds with the position of the Earth on 9th November, and the descending node on 7th May. This means that transits can occur only on or near these dates. However, conditions are not precisely the same for the two dates. At the time of a November transit, Mercury is closer to the Sun than in May, and in addition the apparent diameter of the Sun as seen from the Earth is greater. Thus a November transit can take place even when inferior conjunction occurs as much as five days to either side of the 9th. For a May transit, on the other hand, the maximum is three days before or after the node. Consequently, November transits are much more frequent than transits in May.

The minimum time-lapse between successive transits of Mercury is three years, and the maximum is thirteen; there are thus about 13 transits of the planet each century. Since the orbital periods of the Earth and Mercury do not stand in an exact ratio (while the Earth completes one revolution round the Sun, Mercury completes 4·15207), an almost exact repetition of any particular transit will take place only after 217 years.

The apparent diameter of the disc of Mercury is somewhat greater during May transits, since Mercury is then nearer the Earth than in November, but even so the apparent diameter never exceeds 13 seconds of arc. For this reason Mercury can never be seen with the naked eye during a transit, though Venus is conspicuous against the Sun's face. This explains why there are no records of transits of Mercury until after telescopes had been invented, and astronomers were on the alert for such phenomena.

The first observer to draw attention to transits of Mercury was Johannes Kepler (1571–1630), who in 1627, using tables compiled by himself, predicted the transit of 7th November 1631. Although he did not live to make the observation, it was thanks to his prediction that Pierre Gassendi (1592–1655) saw the transit. Gassendi recorded his observation in a paper, 'Mercurius in Sole Visus', which was published in Amsterdam. Since some two decades elapsed between the invention of the telescope and Kepler's pronouncement in 1627, three transits which observers might have watched passed unnoticed; these took place on 3rd May 1615, 4th November 1618 and 5th May 1628, and were visible in Europe. Most subsequent transits of Mercury have been observed, as the following table shows.

Date	Observer and Location
1631 Nov. 7	Gassendi (Paris)
1644 Nov. 8	(No record)
1651 Nov. 2	Shakerley (Surate, India)
1661 May 3	Hevelius (Danzig)
1664 Nov. 4	(No record)
1677 Nov. 7	Halley (St. Helena)
1690 Nov. 10	? (Canton, China)
1697 Nov. 3	Various (Europe)
1707 May 6	(No record)
1710 Nov. 6	(No record)
1723 Nov. 9	Various (Europe)
1736 Nov. 11	Various (Europe)
1740 May 2	Various (New England)
1743 Nov. 5	Various (Europe)
1753 May 6	Various (Europe)
1756 Nov. 7	? (China, India)
1769 Nov. 9	Various (America)
1776 Nov. 2	(No record) (America)
1782 Nov. 12	Various (Europe)
1786 May 3	Various (Europe)
1789 Nov. 5	Various (Europe)
1799 May 7	Various (Europe)
1802 Nov. 9	Various
1815 Nov. 12	(No record)
1822 Nov. 5	Various
1832 May 5	Various
1835 Nov. 7	Various
1845 May 8	Various

Transits of Mercury

Date	Observer and Location
1848 Nov. 9	Various
1861 Nov. 12	Various
1868 Nov. 5	Various
1878 May 8	Various
1881 Nov. 8	Various
1891 May 8	Various
1894 Nov. 10	Various
1907 Nov. 12	Various
1914 Nov. 6	Various
1924 May 7	Various
1927 Nov. 8	Various
1937 May 10	Various
1940 Nov. 12	Various
1953 Nov. 13	Various
1957 May 6	Various
1960 Nov. 7	Various
1970 May 9	—
1973 Nov. 10	—
1986 Nov. 13	—
1993 Nov. 6	—
1999 Nov. 15	—

[handwritten annotation: 1937 May 10 // Various – non geocentric SUT 40,1, (1970 July) p. 31]

It is, of course, possible that in some cases the transits listed as 'No record' were, in fact, seen; but at least no records of them have come down to us.

Observations of the 1953 transit from stations in Western Europe were made under favourable weather conditions. J. M. Torroja, at the Observatory of Madrid, was responsible for correlating the results. The 1957 transit, however, could not be seen from Europe. The 1960 transit could be partially seen in Central and Western Europe, since first contact took place at 14 h. 34 m. G.M.T. I observed the transit from the Observatory

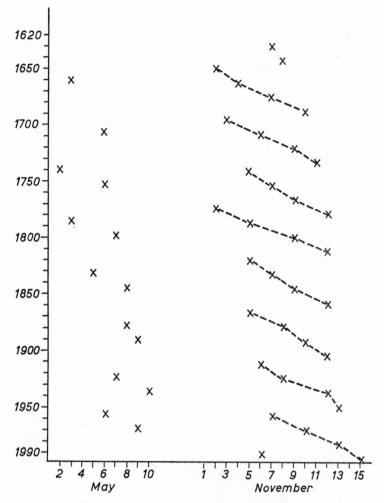

Fig. 10. Transits of Mercury 1631–1999.

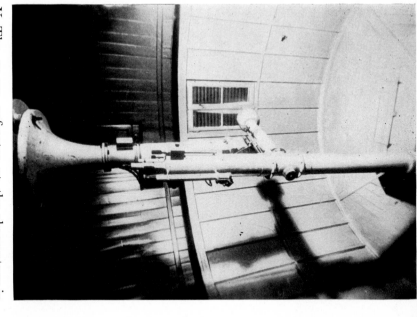

X The 22-cm. refractor at the observatory in Milan used by Schiaparelli for his observations of Mercury. For this work he also used another instrument, the 42-cm. refractor

XI Meudon Observatory, Paris, showing the dome which covers the 33-inch refractor with which Antoniadi carried out his observations of Mercury

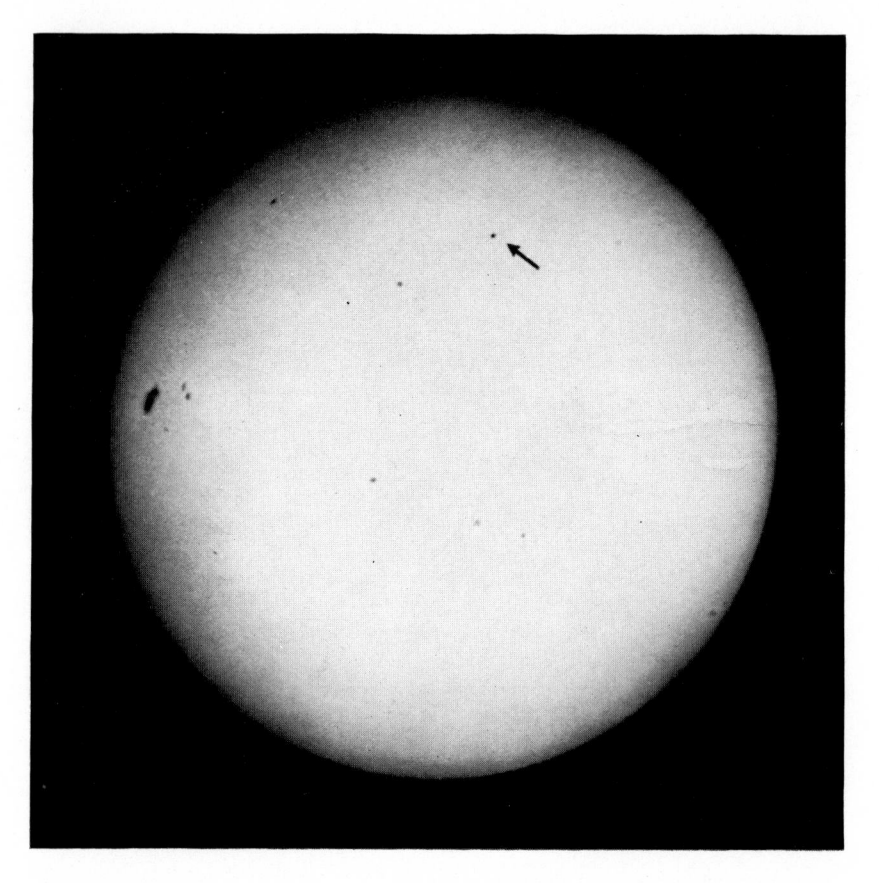

IX Photograph of Sun taken during the transit of Mercury 1960
Nov. 7th, by F. Castillo and G. Raymond. Arrow marks planet

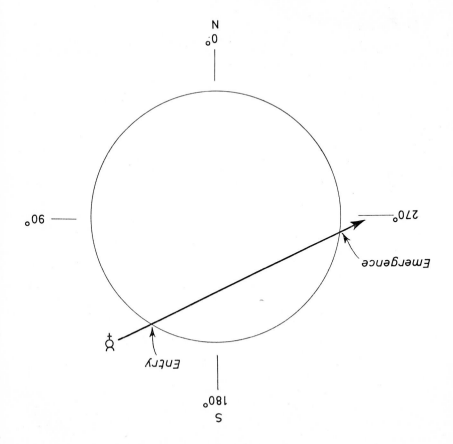

Key to Plate IX. Transit of Mercury 1960 Nov. 7th,
path of planet across face of Sun

of Rome, on the Monte Mario, where weather conditions were better than north of the Alps.

Observers with telescopes may be interested in details concerning the observation regions for transits of Mercury later in this century:

Date of Transit	Observation Regions
1970 May 9	Europe, Africa
1973 Nov. 10	Europe, Africa, Atlantic Ocean
1986 Nov. 13	Asia, Australia, Indian Ocean
1993 Nov. 6	Asia, Australia, Indian Ocean
1999 Nov. 15	Western North America, Pacific Ocean

There is not really a great deal of scientific significance in a transit of Mercury as such; nevertheless, transits are worthwhile phenomena to observe if only for their comparative rarity. The transit of 1677 was an important one in the history of astronomy, since it led Edmond Halley (1656–1742) to discover and compute the method of determining solar parallax by means of transits of Venus. Transits of Mercury have also become important for solving other problems. At one time, for instance, they served to determine the exact orbit of the planet, so that its elements could be revised. It was in this way that Leverrier discovered the irregularities in Mercury's motion which led him to believe in the existence of an intra-Mercurian planet. The connection here with studies of the theory of relativity will be discussed below. Moreover, observations of transits of Mercury have revealed some minute deviations, corresponding to equivalent lunar observations, showing irregularities in the rotation of the Earth.

Observation of a transit of Mercury is carried out in

the following manner. First, note the times of entry or exit of the planet on the solar disc. There are, in fact, four timings which have to be recorded:

1. Entry: exterior contact, when the disc of the planet touches the outer edge of the Sun.

2. Entry: interior contact, when the entire disc of the planet has passed over the limb of the Sun.

3. Emergence: interior contact, when the planet—having passed across the face of the Sun—touches the inside of the limb.

4. Emergence: exterior contact, when the entire disc of the planet has passed across the limb.

The point of the limb of the Sun at which the contact is made is defined by means of the angle, reading from north (0 degrees) through east (90 degrees), south (180 degrees) and west (270 degrees), back to north.

As a result of parallax, the chord along which the planet crosses the Sun is not the same length as seen from different stations. It follows that the length of the chord also determines the duration of the transit. The transit can take as long as $8\frac{1}{2}$ hours if the planet happens to pass right across the centre of the solar disc. This will be more or less the case in 1973 (duration 8 hours); even the transit of 1970 will be a fairly lengthy affair, taking $5\frac{1}{2}$ hours. Conversely, the shorter the chord, the less the duration—right down to very small values, as for the transit of 1999, which will be almost tangential.

The actual processes of entry and emergence each take between 3 and 5 minutes, depending on the position of the chord. During the transit of 1953, for instance, first contact at Madrid took place at 15 h. 35·7 m. G.M.T. and second contact at 15 h. 39·2 m. G.M.T.; third and fourth contacts could not be seen from this location.

The exact determination of the second and third

contacts is not always possible, due to a phenomenon known as the Black Drop. This is a physiological effect where, at the time of second contact, the disc of Mercury appears to remain connected to the Sun's limb by a black strip, which persists even after the planet ought to be clear of the limb. When the strip finally disappears, the planet is already some distance inside the disc, and the precise moment of second contact is past. The effect, also

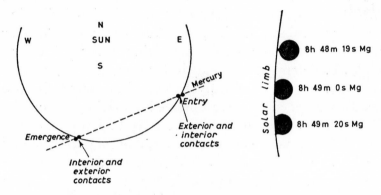

Fig. 11. Transit of Mercury and *black drop* effect, observed by Tebbutt, New South Wales, 7th May 1878.

noticeable for third contact, has caused difficulties—particularly with regard to transits of Venus, which used to be so important in measuring solar parallax. On the other hand, I did not notice it during the 1953 transit of Mercury, when I was in Madrid. It may be that the Black Drop occurs only when atmospheric conditions are not at their best. In contrast to my failure to see it in 1953, I did notice traces of it in 1960, from Rome, when viewing conditions were not quite so good. Brenner also failed to detect it in 1907, either on entry or emergence.

Occasionally there are other somewhat surprising effects. Among these is the appearance of an aureole around the planet's disc, an effect which has already been mentioned during the discussion of a possible atmosphere on Mercury. The first record of such an aureole goes back to 1736, and it was later seen by experienced astronomers such as Fritsch, Schröter, Harding, Schumacher, Schmidt and Huggins. Yet it is worth noting that in 1907 Reboul found that the extent of the aureole remained exactly the same whatever eyepiece was used, indicating that the phenomenon might be an illusion of some kind. A further indication that such might, in fact, be the case is evident, for instance, from the fact that during the 1878 transit C. H. F. Peters (1813–1890) in Clinton, U.S.A., saw the disc of Mercury uniformly black, while Baron O. von Litborn claimed to have detected a bright spot on the S.E. limb on the same day. In 1894 L. Kropp in Pay-sandú (Uruguay) went one better, claiming that he had seen two white specks which persisted throughout the transit, diametrically opposed, one near the S.E. limb of Mercury, the other near the N.W. limb.

Time and again observers have claimed to have seen a tiny bright point on the small, dark disc of Mercury, and Antoniadi gives a long list of such observations in his paper. The first report of such a sighting was made by J. P. Wurzelbauer (1651–1725) of Nuremberg. The more imaginative astronomers of the last century believed that this light emanated from a volcanic outburst at the time of observation, but it is now generally accepted that here too the effect is due to an optical illusion. The human eye is not a sufficiently perfect instrument to be reliable when studying such fine details.

XIV

Mercury and the Theory of Relativity

———————— * ————————

It has already been mentioned that the motion of the perihelion of Mercury's orbit shows an excess of 40 seconds of arc per century, a fact which for many years defied explanation. The value was first given by Leverrier in 1859. It was later corroborated by Simon Newcomb (1835–1909), who took into account all the observational data, including meridian-circle and transit measures, and arrived at a value of 43 seconds.

After the rejection of Leverrier's theory that the excess was due to the influence of an intra-Mercurian planet, various other suggestions were put forward. The most plausible of these was advanced in 1906 by Hugo von Seeliger (1849–1924), who believed that the material comprising the Zodiacal Light might be responsible.

Ten years later, in 1916, Albert Einstein (1879–1955), on the basis of his General Theory of Relativity, came to the conclusion that the precession of the perihelion of a planetary orbit must be rather more rapid than as given by the 'classical' or Newtonian theory of celestial mechanics. He wrote, in 1921: 'The fact can also be expressed thus: According to the General Theory of Relativity, the major axis of the ellipse rotates in the direction of the orbital motion about the Sun. In the case of Mercury, this rotation is said to be 43 seconds of arc in 100 years' (*vide* 'The Special and General Theory of Relativity').

This provides one of the main astronomical proofs of Einstein's theory, and has therefore assumed a great deal of significance during the last few decades. According to the Theory of Relativity, the following precessions are to be expected:

Mercury: 43·03 seconds of arc per 100 years
Venus: 8·6   ,,   ,,   ,,
Earth: 3·8   ,,   ,,   ,,

The effect is therefore most marked in the case of Mercury, and is moreover more easily measured. So far as Venus is concerned, observational proof is very much more difficult to establish, partly because the value is so much less, and partly because the planet's orbit is so nearly circular (the orbital eccentricity of Venus is less than that of any other planet in the Solar System). This means that the position of the perihelion of Venus cannot be measured with the same degree of precision as for Mercury.

In 1939, in the course of work along these lines carried out at Washington under the direction of G. M. Clemence, all the positions of Mercury obtained since 1765 were subjected to new and more detailed scrutiny, involving the examination of 10,000 individual observations, after which the results were compared with the value given by the Theory of Relativity. The observed value was 42·84 seconds of arc, which was not far from the predicted value; indeed, the difference amounted only to a few tenths of a second of arc.

Towards the middle of the 1950s the problem was again attacked at the U.S. Naval Observatory at

Washington, this time by R. L. Duncombe. The following values were obtained:

Mercury: 43·11 seconds of arc
Venus: 8·4   „   „
Earth: 5·9   „   „

which again agree excellently with the values given by relativity theory.

In this way, then, the smallest of the major planets has proved to be a decisive factor in solving some of the more important scientific problems of recent times.

DATA FOR MERCURY

(From *Popular Astronomy*, by Newcomb-Engelmann)

Mean distance from Sun	57,870,000 km. = 0·387099 A.U.
Minimum distance from Sun	0·31 A.U.
Maximum distance from Sun	0·47 A.U.
Light-period at maximum distance of Mercury from the Sun	3m. 54s.
Light-period at minimum distance of Mercury from the Sun	2m. 34s.
Eccentricity of orbit	0·205624
Longitude of perihelion	76·646 degrees
Longitude of ascending node	47·715 degrees
Inclination of orbit to Ecliptic	7·004 degrees
Length of orbit	360,000,000 km.
Mean orbital velocity	47·83 km./sec.
Sidereal period	0·2408 years = 87·97 days
Synodic period	0·3172 years = 115·88 days
Maximum distance from Earth	220,000,000 km.
Minimum distance from Earth	79,000,000 km.
Maximum apparent diameter	12·9 seconds of arc
Minimum apparent diameter	4·7 seconds of arc
Actual diameter	4800 km.= 0·38 Earth
Polar compression	Nil
Volume	$5·79 \times 10^{10}$ km^3 = 0·053 Earth

Data for Mercury

Mass*	3.31×10^{25}gr. =
	0.055 Earth =
	1/6,000,000 Sun
Gravitational acceleration at surface	3.84×10^2 cm./sec.^{2} =
	0.39 Earth
Density	5.72 water = 1.04 Earth
Rotation Period	87.97 days
Inclination of equator to plane of orbit	20 degrees (?)
Albedo	0.07
Maximum magnitude	−1.6
Minimum magnitude	+1.7

*A new evaluation of the mass of Mercury has recently been published in the Soviet Union. Since Mercury does not have a satellite, the two scientists responsible, S. G. Makower and N. A. Bochan, decided to base their calculations on the perturbatory effect exercised by the planet on Enke's Comet. The result of their findings: Mass of Mercury = (1/5,880,000 ± 1/200,000) Mass of Sun.

MAPS OF MERCURY

The number of charts of the surface of Mercury so far published is extremely limited. The most important are those compiled by Schiaparelli, Antoniadi and the observers at the Pic du Midi.

Year	Author	Source
1889	G. V. Schiaparelli	'Sulla rotazione di Mercurio' (*Astronomische Nachrichten*, No. 2944, vol. 123)
1896	P. Lowell	'New Observations of the Planet Mercury' (*Memoirs* of the American Academy of Arts and Sciences, Vol. XII)
1920	R. Jarry-Desloges	'Observations des Surfaces Planétaires'
1936	E. M. Antoniadi	'La Planète Mercure et la Rotation des Satellites'
1936	H. McEwen	'The Markings of Mercury' (*Journal* of the British Astronomical Association, *46*, 10)
1947	W. H. Haas	'A Ten-Year Study of the Planet Mercury and its Atmosphere' (*Popular Astronomy*, *LV*, 3)
1948	L. Rudaux	'L'Astronomie, Les Astres, L'Univers'

Year	Author	Source
1953	Pic du Midi	*L'Astronomie*, February 1953, p. 65
1960	G. Wegner	*Strolling Astronomer*, *14*, December 1960

Index